8-95

concilium 1998/2

THE ETHICS OF GENETIC ENGINEERING

Edited by

Maureen Junker-Kenny and
Lisa Sowle Cahill

SCM Press · London
Orbis Books · Maryknoll

Published by SCM Press Ltd, 9–17 St Albans Place, London N1
and by Orbis Books, Maryknoll, NY 10545

ISBN: 0 334 03048 X (UK)
ISBN: 1 57075 188 9 (USA)

Typeset at The Spartan Press Ltd, Lymington, Hants
Printed by Biddles Ltd, Guildford and King's Lynn

Concilium Published February, April, June, October, December.

Contents

Editorial

Genetics, Ethics and Social Policy: The State of the Question

Lisa Sowle Cahill

Although the categories of genetic science overlap to some extent, some basic ones are: diagnosis of genetic disease (including preimplantation diagnosis, prenatal diagnosis, genetic tests on children, screening for workplace and insurance, diagnostic kits for self-diagnosis, diagnosis of predispositions to genetic disease, and population screening, as well as the definitions of health and confidentiality); eugenics as the elimination of disease-related traits (through selective mating, sterilization, or detection and elimination of affected embryos or foetuses); gene therapy (germ-line or somatic); genetic enhancement (germ-line or somatic); patenting human gene sequences or techniques of genetic control; embryo research; cloning; and genetic testing on controlled groups of research subjects, including comparative trials with placebos.

The opportunity to use new genetic techniques, like prenatal genetic diagnosis or gene therapy, is available largely in the industrialized nations. Even within this limited realm, the practical circumstances and cultural contexts of genetic medicine and research vary significantly. More importantly, however, advances in genetics affect attitudes toward life, death and health; actual availability of biomedical resources; and research practices, in many other cultures where most of the population will never have the opportunity to share the benefits of advanced genetics. Yet emerging international policy on genetics is controlled primarily by the 'First World', and it is developing slowly, at an uneven pace, and with significant inconsistencies from region to region. Moreover, the legal authority of national and international policy directives varies greatly.

One of the most significant investors in genetics research, the United States, has few legally enforced internal restrictions on genetics research as long as it is privately funded, fewer restrictions on publicly funded research than many European nations place on all research, and no legal restrictions on actions that researchers may take in other countries. Meanwhile, European countries are voting individually whether to ratify 'The Convention on Human Rights and Biomedicine' of the 'Steering Committee on Bioethics' of the forty-member Council of Europe.[1] But populations in developing nations have few protections against profit-driven research funded by technologically advanced nations, both because of the lack of effective global supervision, and because poorer nations are reluctant to enact internal regulations that would discourage much-needed investment by business in the 'First World'. The most universal policy-making body, the United Nations, does not have the legal authority to enforce its statement on genetics, although it does mention in general terms the need to respect the dignity and rights of peoples as well as individuals, and to foster scientific cooperation among industrialized and developing nations.[2]

International policy on genetics has been concerned primarily with manipulation of the individual genotype, and therefore with germ line versus somatic cell therapy; the difference between therapy and enhancement; cloning; and the use of embryos in genetic research and therapy (either germ line therapy or cloning). To the extent that social ethics has been part of policy debates, it has been limited for the most part to considerations of the social consequences of permissive policies regarding individual choice (of researchers, clinicians or clients) to manipulate the genetic characteristics of specific embryos or persons. Moreover, these debates have occurred largely in the nations with the capacity to fund such research, and with a population of consumers who are able to afford its results (Europe and North America). Greatly lacking in policy debates in these same countries is serious attention to the global social, economic and biomedical scenario, including the international ramifications of the policies and actions of the North Atlantic industrialized nations. And even within these nations, the moral criteria applied to genetics reflect a rather narrow, liberal, late-modern philosophical and political tradition: freedom of choice, pragmatic benefits and 'social acceptance' in these same cultures. Yet, as Dietmar Mieth points out, it is not adequate to approach the new ethical problems posed by genetics as though the person, or personal interests, liberties and options, could be considered apart from the social institutions that define the very project of realizing personhood. 'Persons are ultimately morally responsible for institutions, and institutions present a conditional framework within which persons can perceive their moral responsibility.'[3] The topic of genetics and ethics highlights the problem of understanding and shaping global as well as local institutions.

That specific policies in the United States and in Europe are being developed with little attention to a globally egalitarian social policy is evident from recent statements of the Council of Europe, the European Commission, the United Nations (UNESCO) and the United States. The Steering Committee on Bioethics of the Council of Europe produced 'The Convention on Human Rights and Biomedicine'. The Convention prohibits genetic discrimination; says diagnostic tests may be used only to find disease; allows gene therapy, but not if it affects the germ line; places a ban on the creation of embryos for research purposes; and requires 'adequate protection' of embryos undergoing research (but does not specify what that entails).[4] It was signed by representatives of twenty-one of the forty member countries in April 1997, with other countries' representatives gradually joining. In each country, the signature of its delegate to the Council of Europe must be followed by a process of ratification that actually makes the provisions of the Convention legally binding. (However, it does not supersede any stricter legislation that may already exist, e.g., the total ban on embryo research in Germany.)

The Convention has also been signed (not yet ratified) by eleven of the fifteen member states of the European Commission (the government of the European Community). The endorsement of the member states of the European Union does not have the direct force of law, but does imply that it will be respected by the European Union and eventually ratified as law broadly in Europe. The Group of Advisors of the European Commission also issued a separate advisory (not legally binding) document, 'Ethical Aspects of Cloning' (May 1997). The European Commission's Directive on Patenting Biotechnological Inventions permitted embryo research on cloning techniques, but includes a ban on implantation of a cloned embryo. Finally UNESCO (United Nations Educational, Scientific and Cultural Organization) has produced a 'Universal Declaration on the Human Genome and Human Rights' which was signed in November 1997, that also includes a ban on germ line therapy, says there shall be no discrimination against individuals on the basis of genetic information, and excludes so-called 'reproductive cloning'. This declaration is not legally binding.

The major difference between emerging European law and US law is that The Convention on Human Rights and Biomedicine, when ratified in a given country, will apply to all research, whether publicly or privately funded. For those receiving US government funding, the creation of embryos for research purposes is currently banned by Federal Statute and Presidential Order, and the President called on all other researchers to respect this ban voluntarily. In its 1997 National Institutes of Health appropriations bill, the Congress extended a one-year ban to all federally-funded embryo research. The National Bioethics Advisory Commission, which issued a report on human cloning in June 1997, after a three-month study, advised a three-to-five year federal ban on all human cloning, however funded, but that ban has not yet been enacted by legislation. Other differences are that the Convention of the Council of Europe explicitly forbids discrimination based on genetic information, limits modification of the human genome to therapies for disease, and prohibits any modification that will alter the genome of offspring. These issues are not addressed under US policy.

Discussions about germ line therapy, especially in Europe, reveal ways in which genetics challenges standard patterns of moral analysis, even if we set aside innovations like cloning, and consider only the apparently benign use of genetics to heal disease. An obvious problem is defining health. But an even larger question is whether it is really possible to consider germ line gene therapy 'in itself', without also taking into the analysis the embryo research that would be necessary to produce it, possible effects on future generations, the facility with which it would be possible to pass from germ line therapy to enhancements, and the likelihood that social classes that already have access to money and technology would use this new advantage to further self-interest, and in disregard for the welfare of the other persons, present and future. In 1994, UNESCO accepted germ line therapy for disease, while the European Commission (GAEIB) denied its legitimacy 'at the present time', stipulating that equal access and the 'transparency' of research and clinical applications would have to be guaranteed first. In 1995, the British Science and Technology Committee held that no germ line therapy could be done without the approval of the Genetic Therapy Advisory Committee, but left undefined the conditions under which such permission would be granted, and whether it would be based on the interests of individual couples, or on the common good. In Germany, a debate in 1993–94 led to a consensus against germ line therapy, as stated in the 1995 Bundesarztekammer guidelines. Recent German history has created a distrust of bioethics, suspicion of ideas like 'selection', and unwillingness to separate abstract philosophical justifications of germ line therapy 'in itself' from the context in which it would be developed and implemented. Anglo-American philosophical and policy reasoning tends to be much more focussed on the individual rather than society, on liberty rather than the common good, and on the freedom of research rather than its social control, as well as to place the burden of proof on those advising caution.[5]

A narrow approach to such new innovations as germ line therapy and cloning is inadequate. For instance, the internationally sponsored Human Genome Project, that plans to map the entire genome by 2005, presents much larger questions about the relation of genetic information to personal identity, social relations, and social control of science and technology. Similarly, attempts to patent techniques for obtaining and utilizing information about genetic sequences presents enormous philosophical, ethical and social questions about the emergence of a 'biotechnology industry' that profits by controlling the results of genetics research.

Areas of ethical and policy debate in which social considerations beyond individual choice are beginning to enter the discussion about genetics are patenting, population screening, testing of genetic therapies, and health insurance (primarily in the US, still lacking universal health care). However, policy even in these areas is still dominated by market considerations. In other words, influential parties to the discussion who stand to benefit financially (or in terms of research prestige, which amounts to the same thing) are often successful in shaping policy so that it permits the practices that serve their interests.

For example, there is no genetic research on malaria, because Africa is not a profitable market, even though such research might have the potential to serve many people in a more radical way than some currently funded research. In a market environment, free choice by those with assets controls access to benefits, and even defines what benefits will be available. An article that appeared in an American newspaper in late 1997 reported that, at the University of Pittsburgh, a researcher on a somatic cell genetic therapy for muscular dystrophy has already been approached by a sports medicine doctor in the US, who wanted access to a treatment that could make healthy players grow larger muscles. Another researcher at the University of Minnesota reported that he had had an inquiry about changing skin colour to simulate membership in a preferred race.[6] In a liberal market system, individuals giving 'informed consent' may decide their own eugenic agenda, on the basis of what they can afford.

Although there is some recognition that 'commodification' of embryos, children, or genetic knowledge may be a moral problem for society as a whole, this concern is usually subordinated to informed consent. The intersections of economic institutions with those of medicine, parenthood and family is not critically examined, but taken for granted. An exception may be the cautious approach that most national and international policies are now adopting toward human cloning. But even in this case, no one of the major policy-making bodies has placed an absolute and permanent ban on cloning. In fact, by placing restrictions only on cloning that actually results in the birth of a child, policies in Europe and North America permit the refinement of techniques that will eventually lead to the births of cloned individuals; and in effect, encourage 'First World' researchers to perfect their techniques at home, then move to less regulated countries when they are ready to produce a baby.

If we look at genetics and ethics from the standpoint of social ethics, it is clear that two important factors are missing in most international policy debates: 1. the influence of the *market* in determining what research is funded, where it is done, and who benefits from its applications; and 2. the possibility of beginning a more inclusive dialogue about genetics and ethics that would incorporate wider *global* participation, including *grassroots* participation. Discussion about genetics, ethics and social policy is now controlled almost exclusively by the academic, political and scientific élites in the First World nations of Europe and North America. This perspective does not offer an adequate base for making decisions about practices that in fact affect the lives and futures of much larger populations. However, the fact that multinational organizations in Europe are beginning to create forums for discussion of genetics and ethics is a promising sign. The greatest obstacle to justice in global practices of genetic research and therapy will remain the self-interest of those who retain control over the acquisition of genetic knowledge and its application. Genetics provides yet another illustration of the most fundamental problem of social ethics: the redistribution of power in a competitive atmosphere in which there is no effective and fair arbiter of conflicting interests and claims.

Notes

1. For a history of the Convention, and a comparison with US law, see F. William Dommel, Jr and Duane Alexander, 'The Convention on Human Rights and Biomedicine of the Council of Europe', *Kennedy Institute of Ethics Journal* 7/3, 1997, 259–76.
2. Committee of Governmental Experts for the Finalization of a Draft Declaration on the Human Genome, UNESCO, 'Draft of a Universal Declaration on the Human Genome and Human Rights', Paris, July 1997.
3. Dietmar Mieth, 'The Problem of "Justified Interests" in Genome Analysis: A

Socioethical Approach', in Hille Haker, Richard Hearn, Klaus Steigleden (eds), *Ethics of Human Genome Analysis: European Perspectives*, Tübingen 1995, 277. Mieth is professor of theological ethics and chairman of the Ethics in Science Centre at the University of Tübingen, a member of the European Commission's Group of Advisors on the Ethical Implications of Biotechnology, and head of the European Network for Biomedical Ethics.

4. The Convention is published in the *Kennedy Institute of Ethics Journal* 7/3, 1997.

5. Dietmar Mieth, 'A Survey of Ethical Questions Concerning Gene Therapy', in Stefan Müller, Jürgen W. Simon and Jan W. Vesting (eds), *Interdisciplinary Approaches to Gene Therapy. Legal, Ethical and Scientific Aspects*, Berlin, Heidelberg and New York 1997, 197–211.

6. Rich Weiss, 'Gene Enhancements' Thorny Ethical Traits: Rapid-Fire Discoveries Force Examination of Consequences', *The Washington Post*, Sunday, 12 October 1997, p. A1.

1 · Human Genetics and Human Control

Genetic Knowledge as a Commodity: The Human Genome Project, Markets and Consumers

Julie Clague

The complex macromolecule DNA – which is found within the chromosomes contained in every cell of the body – is made up of thousands of gene segments whose molecular structures provide the necessary instructions for body cells to produce the proteins required for human existence. The current state of knowledge about the purpose and function of genes is very limited. Only a small fraction of the estimated 100,000 human genes are known and few of these are understood. The Human Genome Project (HGP) is an ambitious international collaborative venture to chart the genetic blueprint, locating the positions of all the genes on the chromosomes, and sequencing all the genetic information that is encoded within them. The task of mapping and sequencing the genetic material in the twenty-four unique chromosomes (the genome) is enormous: the project began officially on 1 October 1990 and is expected to take over a decade to complete. The information gained from the project will be stored in databases around the world and will help unravel the remaining mysteries of human development, disease and demise.

The HGP is expected to revolutionize knowledge of genetics – providing clues about embryonic development, the onset of death and the process of evolution – and to yield benefits which will transform human living. It is possible that a fuller understanding of the role which genes play in our lives may open up interesting avenues to pursue in the field of ethics concerning the extent to which genes define capabilities, predispositions and characteristics, both physical and emotional; which, in turn, could provoke reflection on the nature of human freedom and culpability. This exploration would be a part of the wider quest for a deeper and more truthful account of human 'nature', since much ethics of late has been concerned to elaborate on how culture, historical situatedness, gender and a variety of other such factors influence our world view and self-understanding. And, though reductionists have been keen to tie down nature through the application of narrow simplifications such as the tendency to genetic determinism, it seems more likely that, rather than resolve the eternal nature/nurture debate in one direction or the other, genetic knowledge will illustrate instead the complex interrelationship between the two.

Most attention has focussed on the medical benefits of the project. Faulty genes disrupt the body's protein-making processes causing over 5,000 diseases known to affect humans. Knowledge about the genetic basis of disease will grow: not just monogenic disorders, but multifactorial diseases such as cancer and coronary heart disease in which genetic predisposition plays a role. New diagnostic tests are becoming available that detect whether an individual carries defective genes that have the potential to cause disease in that person or to contribute to genetic disorders in offspring. Until recently scientists have been limited to tackling the biochemical consequences of disease rather than the genetic source. Now, there is the prospect of gene therapy techniques to correct, switch off or replace faulty genes. Ultimately, the goal is the prevention and treatment of diseases with a genetic component. As yet, however, therapeutic interventions remain a future aspiration. A very substantial time-lag is anticipated between the commercial availability of diagnostic tests and the ability to prevent or treat genetic disorders. Hence the establishment of genetic counselling services to help individuals and families understand and manage genetic disorder and to make informed reproductive decisions on the basis of probable risks.

The genetic advances made possible by the HGP bring with them a host of complex ethical issues. Some of the more urgent concerns which have been identified include questions of privacy and confidentiality raised by the genetic testing of individuals and the screening of large populations: both in terms of the duty to inform family members of one's genetic status, and in light of the interest shown in genetic testing by insurance companies and employers. The availability of genetic tests for diseases which have no existing treatment has raised concerns about the potentially damaging effects of knowledge concerning the future health and life expectancy of persons and their offspring, and about how such knowledge might influence reproductive and end-of-life decisions. Unknown at this stage is the effect of genetic information about health, capabilities and dispositions on social attitudes towards 'normality'. The mistreatment of people with syphilis, HIV/AIDS and many other diseases highlights the potential for prejudice and discrimination; hence international legislative efforts to make discrimination based on a person's genome illegal.

Questions of whether and in what way the human genome should be modified arise in light of the prospects of gene therapy – especially in cases where the genetic inheritance of future generations stands to be affected in addition to the consenting individual treated. Could some improvements to a person's genetic make-up be immoral? At what point might correction of a disorder (dwarfism, say) become cosmetic enhancement, and in what circumstances is cosmetic enhancement justified?

Successes in animal cloning have led to suggestions that cloning techniques (currently outlawed on humans) might one day be combined with germ line gene therapy in order to assist couples who are guaranteed to produce embryos with a particular genetic deficiency. The DNA from an early embryo could be corrected by inserting a functioning gene and then implanted into a new egg cell, thereby replacing the original defective embryo with a healthy clone of itself: this would be genetically identical except for the modification. The genetic disorder would be removed both for the new embryo and subsequent generations. In the loss of early, defective embryos a price worth paying to obtain healthy replacements?

Human gene material can be injected into animal eggs to create transgenic animals. The animal's milk or other products may then be used as sources of vital human proteins which otherwise would be in short supply or expensive to obtain. It may also become possible to rear genetically modified animals which provide transplant organs resistant to rejection by the human immune system. This will raise important questions. For example, to what extent do the possibilities of using transgenic animals count as 'tampering' with the created order? And should such interventions in nature be judged solely on the basis of their foreseeable consequences or are questions of intrinsic meaning at stake?

There will never be a single ethical focus in discussion of the HGP. As fresh possibilities and challenges emerge from the project, the focus will shift to include other ethical issues – questions of justice, autonomy, consent, beneficence and so on – which are not unique to the HGP but are newly juxtaposed. The substantial nature of these issues prompted both the US and European genome organizations to allocate a fixed percentage of their genome budgets to activities which address the ethical, legal and social implications of the project. By 1998, the US genome organization alone will have distributed approximately $40 million in research and education grants to projects exploring ethical, legal and social issues.[1]

As the project evolves, it is increasingly clear that many of the ethical issues raised by the HGP cannot be viewed in isolation from the financial motivations fuelling the project. The HGP is of great importance to the economic interests of developed nations. All estimates of the cost of the HGP run into billions of dollars. Those at the forefront of this investment – the United States, Japan and the European nations – expect lucrative returns in terms of commercial applications for their biotechnology industries. The genetic information obtained from the project is expected to inspire countless innovations. In short, the HGP concerns the transformation of scientific knowledge into a marketable commodity. The process by which such a transformation takes place has been exposed to critical scrutiny by Jean-François Lyotard in his essay *The Postmodern Condition*, which examines the relationship between knowledge, science and technology in advanced capitalist societies:

> The relationship of the suppliers and users of knowledge to the knowledge they supply and use is now tending, and will increasingly tend, to assume the form already taken by the relationship of commodity producers and consumers to the commodities they produce and consume – that is, the form of value. Knowledge is and will be produced in order to be sold, it is and will be consumed in order to be valorized in a new production: in both cases, the goal is exchange.[2]

However, it is not just the interests of commerce which greets the birth of new scientific knowledge, but also politics:

> Knowledge in the form of an informational commodity indispensable to productive power is already, and will continue to be, a major – perhaps *the* major – stake in the worldwide competition for power. It is conceivable that the nation-states will one day fight for control of information, just as they battled in the past for control over territory, and afterwards for control of access to and exploitation of raw materials and cheap labour. A new field is opened for industrial and commercial strategies on the one hand, and political and military strategies on the other.[3]

It is technology that links science to the economy by transforming knowledge into a product or production technique through invention and innovation. Businesses imitate those products or production techniques which are marketable. This is the crucial process on which the developed nations – as financial backers of the HGP – are relying. In the market, financial incentives and competition ensure a constant effort to improve and refine products and production techniques. In Lyotard's words, technology follows the principle of 'performativity', or

> the principle of optimal performance: maximizing output (the information or modifications obtained) and minimizing input (the energy expended in the process). Technology is therefore a game pertaining not to the true, the just, or the beautiful, etc, but to efficiency: a technical 'move' is 'good' when it does better and/or expends less energy than another.[4]

Technological efficiency and cost-effectiveness (financial efficiency) are rewarded with commercial success which, in turn, generates the capital to refine the product's performance further. Efficiency is, as Michael Novak observes, one of the defining features of democratic capitalism: 'If democratic capitalism has conferred enormous wealth upon the world . . . it has also proven to be the most *efficient* system ever devised by human beings.'[5] Democratic capitalism is efficient because industries which are inefficient do not survive. The persistence of human striving for efficiency in the production of marketable commodities is a necessary response to the market's demand for wealth creation.

The HGP provides a vivid illustration of Lyotard's thesis. Considerable investment is currently directed towards the development of profitable diagnostic tests and new pharmaceutical products, such as those which exist for insulin and human growth hormone. Efficiency is maximized at laboratory level by the application of large-scale factory production methods to the repetitive and largely automated mapping and sequencing work. The criterion of cost-effectiveness was applied by those charged with assessing the feasibility of the HGP at its genesis during the mid-1980s. Fear of wasteful duplication of work led to the initial decision to co-ordinate the international research effort. Collaboration and information-sharing reduces costs and speeds up processes. As Robert Cook-Deegan explains:

> Constructing maps and developing technologies in an organized fashion would prove far more efficient than hoping that complete maps would emerge from thousands of uncoordinated searches for individual genes . . . Efficiency of resource allocation was invoked as the principle justification for the Human Genome Project.[6]

However, as gene segments have become identified with particular diseases, commercial interest has led to attempts to patent them. It is widely assumed that patents provide the best means of encouraging the investment in research and product development necessary for the growth of the biotechnology industry. In such circumstances, free flow of knowledge is perceived to be a hindrance to the operation of the market. Competition and secrecy become the dominant modes of behaviour, because that is what the market demands. Although it is by no means likely that genetic testing in the workplace will be permitted, it is clear that the mooted use of genetic testing by employers is an attempt to predict which people make the most cost-effective employees, that is, those workers who give the best returns on the company's investment in them. The HGP highlights the dominant theme of optimal performance in the operation of the global economy, and the patenting of gene sequences reveals the commercial value of scientific knowledge.

The medical advances promised by the HGP will result largely from successful product development by biotechnology companies. Social benefit is therefore tied to the market, for the medical goals and the economic goals of the project are interrelated. However, the immediate beneficiaries of the HGP, both economically and medically, will be the developed nations, which does not bode well for global justice. The challenge for the HGP is identified by Bernadine Healy:

> We should explore ways for [developing] countries to be included among those receiving the social benefits accrued from the development of genetic information, without diminishing the commercial incentives required to promote substantial investments in the development of products created from basic discoveries that will ultimately benefit everyone.[7]

How can this be achieved? Goods and benefits do not 'trickle down' to developing countries either as easily or as speedily as might be wished. All too often, geographical short-sightedness on the part of developed nations sees problems closer to home as the most pressing. As with the initial research into HIV/AIDS (funded and performed in the developed world), the initial focus of attention in human genome research has been on the medical disorders of Caucasians. The cystic fibrosis gene, which 1 in 25 North Europeans carry, is one of the most studied parts of the human genome. Instead of relying on a 'trickle down' effect, there is a need to promote the growth of scientific research and technological innovation within developing countries. However, the economic obstacles to this proposal are considerable, as Lyotard suggests:

> It is widely accepted that knowledge has become the principle force of production over the last few decades; this has already had a noticeable effect on the composition of the work force of the most highly developed

countries and constitutes the major bottleneck for the developing countries. In the post-industrial and postmodern age, science will maintain and no doubt strengthen its pre-eminence in the arsenal of productive capacities of the nation-states. Indeed, this situation is one of the reasons leading to the conclusion that the gap between developed and developing countries will grow ever wider in the future.[8]

Developing countries are prevented from entering the market as full participants, either as producers or consumers: 'no technology without wealth, but no wealth without technology.'[9] Is a just distribution of goods and benefits between the developing and developed world attainable in the global marketplace? The key question to ask in this regard is what drives the need to do what is just. It seems that those in power – whose responsibility it is to keep the economic machine in motion – are motivated to act only when the market responds to a fairer distribution of benefits by increased performance: '[The decision makers] allocate our lives for the growth of power. In matters of social justice and of scientific truth alike, the legitimation of that power is based on its optimizing the system's performance – efficiency.'[10] Lyotard's essay, written before the genetic revolution, is prophetic.

The drive towards efficiency in the HGP will deliver medical benefits, such as useful diagnostic tools, sooner than would otherwise be possible. As a goal, efficiency is valuable. However, there is a tendency, particularly prevalent in affluent societies, which is overly-concerned with its promotion. This view has been given powerful expression in Pope John Paul II's encyclical letter *Evangelium Vitae*, which describes the emergence of a culture 'actively fostered by powerful cultural, economic and political currents which encourage an idea of society excessively concerned with efficiency'.[11] Within this impoverished world-view, human progress is measured in terms of technological control over nature, and personal fulfilment determined by the degree of control over one's destiny. In both cases the goal is to optimize life; to improve performance; to eliminate fate. Humankind has learnt to bend nature to its purposes. Scientific knowledge has led to some degree of control over health. New economic and political circumstances provide an unprecedented degree of personal autonomy. As a result, humans have broken free from many of the determining factors which previously controlled their lives. Humans both exercise their freedom and assert control over their destiny through the choices they make about their life-style. In the developed world, the term 'citizen' is no longer adequate to describe the person's role in society. It has been replaced by the term 'consumer'. Market forces are simply the measure of consumers making choices about goods and services. John Paul II identified the dangers inherent in consumerism in his encyclical letter *Centesimus Annus*:

> A given culture reveals its overall understanding of life through the choices it makes in production and consumption. It is here that *the phenomenon of consumerism* arises ... *Thus a great deal of educational and cultural work* is urgently needed, including the education of consumers in the responsible use of their power of choice ...[12]

New technological developments, such as those heralded by the HGP, are presented in terms of increasing choice for the consumer. Consider, for example, the techniques of pre-natal and pre-implantation testing of foetuses and embryos for genetic abnormalities. Since gene therapy is not yet available as a choice which consumers are able to make for themselves or their children, and since the consumer society is geared towards an ideal of human perfection, would-be parents are increasingly offered an alternative route to the perfect baby. Pre-natal screening detects foetal abnormalities for which the pregnant woman can be offered a termination of pregnancy. Pre-implantation diagnosis detects certain genetic disorders in the early embryo *in vitro*. It can be offered to those parents known to be at risk of conceiving a child with an inherited disease. The parents can proceed with pregnancy in the case of healthy embryos, and discard affected embryos without the necessity for termination of pregnancy. Pre-implantation diagnosis will become increasingly common as genetic knowledge grows and new genetic tests become available.

How do such practices relate to the goals of genetic medicine? Genetic medicine aims at something which cannot yet fully be delivered: to identify and correct genetic disorders by manipulating genes, thereby benefitting individual human beings and simultaneously improving the gene pool for future generations. Human desire to improve the gene pool is not new. Historically, it has been associated with the eugenics movement, a motley group combining an obsession with an image of human perfection with a misplaced scientism, in which quasi-scientific methods of improving the quality of the human race were applied through selective breeding techniques, of the sort first used in animal husbandry. Until gene therapy techniques are developed, selection remains the sole means of improving the gene pool. The difference is that, in the past, those in a position of power or influence attempted to quell the reproductive habits of those who were considered to have 'bad genes'. This reached its nadir in the compulsory state-controlled programme of the Nazis. Now selection is democratized. Choices can be taken by individual consumers. Families are free to determine their own genetic futures; they decide which genetic disorders to tolerate. Pre-natal and pre-implantation testing is carried out under the banner of responsible parenthood: on the basis of promoting what is considered to be in the best interests of existing family members. In the past, eugenics programmes were aimed at what authorities (mistakenly) believed to be in the best interests of both the nation-state and future generations in general. Is this a triumph for autonomy?

It is well to be aware that reproductive decisions taken on the basis of genetic knowledge take shape within an economic climate in which particular values are prevalent, and in which the dominant life-style choices of others in society place indirect pressure on those who share a different conception of humanity. The consumer has some degree of freedom but is also, to some degree, slave to the majority's interests. Policies (institutionalized choices based on the criterion of cost-effectiveness and public approval) influence the choices of consumers. Those who impede the efficient running of the system by making unpopular and/or unsustainable choices, and those – such as people with disabilities – viewed as incurring a cost to society, may be greeted with intolerance. People will be tolerated in so far as they are recognized as contributing to the sustenance of the economic machine. The genetic choices which will be required of individuals in the future will, at the same time, be both moral decisions with economic ramifications and economic decisions with moral ramifications. Consumers both shape and are shaped by economic forces.

The immediate impact of the HGP on universal health care will not be great. Many of the serious health problems facing both the developed and developing worlds are not genetic in character. Important factors which affect a person's risk of contracting disease include place of birth, social class, economic well-being and the medical provision available. Premature deaths, particularly in developing countries, continue to be caused by factors related to poor nutrition and living conditions which are a direct result of economic disadvantage. The depressing facts concerning human health and disease are a reminder that the HGP is not the answer to all of humanity's medical problems. The social benefits, medical and economic, that the HGP will eventually deliver will continue to tax humans on the means of their just distribution long after their availability to the relative few.

Technical progress may supply the material for human advance but it is powerless to actualize it.[13]

For the HGP genuinely to be recognized as furthering human progress it must achieve more than mere technological advance. It must inspire moral progress too, in which human benefit is distributed widely: not just to those in the developed nations that can afford the technology, and not just to the majority who do not have a genetic disability. For progress is not something that can be obtained for one at the expense of another. If history teaches us anything, its surest lesson must be this.

Notes

1. Cf. Eric M. Meslin, Elizabeth J. Thomson and Joy T. Boyer, 'The Ethical, Legal, and Social Implications Research Program at the National Human Genome Research Institute', *Kennedy Institute Of Ethics Journal*, Vol. 7, No. 3, September 1997, 291–8: 292–3.

2. Jean-François Lyotard, *The Postmodern Condition: A Report on Knowledge*, Manchester 1992, 4–5.

3. Ibid., 5.

4. Ibid., 44.

5. Michael Novak, *The American Vision. An Essay on the Future of Democratic Capitalism*, Washington DC, 1978 (as cited in John Atherton, [ed.], *Social Christianity: A Reader*, London 1994, 376).

6. Robert Mullan Cook-Deegan, 'Genome Mapping and Sequencing', in William T. Reich (ed.), *Encyclopedia of Bioethics*, Revised Edition, Vol. 2, New York 1995, 1011–20: 1014–15.

7. Bernadine Healey, 'Special Report on Gene Patenting', *New England Journal of Medicine*, 27 August, 1992, 664–8: 668.

8. Lyotard, *The Postmodern Condition* (n. 2), 5.

9. Ibid., 45.

10. Ibid., xxiv.

11. John Paul II, *Evangelium Vitae (The Gospel Of Life)*, 1995, no. 12.

12. John Paul II, *Centesimus Annus (On The Hundredth Anniversary of Rerum Novarum)*, 1991, no. 36.

13. Vatican II, *Gaudium et Spes, The Pastoral Constitution on the Church in the Modern World*, 1965, no. 35.

Gene Therapy and the Improvement of Human Nature: Ethical Questions

Sandro Spinsanti

I. Stages of genetics, stages of ethics

No form of power that human beings have been able to exercise over nature in the past is comparable with the dominion over life that has been made possible by recent discoveries in the sphere of genetics and by the perfection of technologies which make it possible to intervene in the deepest level of living nature. We have arrived at this point unexpectedly. We can recognize clearly differentiated periods in the development of genetics, which are matched by similar stages in ethics. In fact, each stage of the growth of human knowledge about and power over the mechanism of the transmission of life has mobilized ethical reflection in a different way.

Genetics as the science of heredity, the birth of which was presided over by Mendel little more than a century ago, did not show its potential immediately. Mendel's discoveries, recognized as general laws of heredity only at the beginning of the twentieth century, appeared to have practical consequences only for the founders of eugenics. This movement arose as a project to improve the human species by means of control over procreation, favouring the transmission of promising hereditary characteristics and preventing the reproduction of those characteristics which were thought to be negative. The 1928 edition of *Larousse* stated as the aim of the 'new science' of eugenics to 'eliminate the undesirable elements and to keep and perfect the healthy and robust elements'.

The scientific foundations of eugenics were anything but solid. However, it needed only a veneer of science for eugenic programmes to be undertaken by the Nazi government in Germany in the period between the two world wars – which used eugenics to justify its criminal racist policy – and for other eugenic practices in the Scandinavian countries and the

United States (with the same scientific inconsistency and lack of any results in improving the species but without Nazi totalitarianism). The errors of the past have brought discredit on such authoritarian eugenic programmes, which were also unequivocally condemned from the moral point of view in that they violated the fundamental right of the person to self-determination. The practices based on eugenics did not disappear, but prolonged their existence in a quasi-clandestine way. The law which allowed sterilization for eugenic reasons in Sweden was only abolished in 1976. Recent studies calculate that about 100,000 women in the Scandinavian countries will have been forcibly denied the right to reproduce.

If Mendel's discoveries represent the prehistory, and eugenics the ancient history, of genetics (the improvement of the species by eliminating children with a hereditary defect was, moreover, also practice current in Sparta, with far less brilliant results in terms of the history of civilization than those obtained by Athens), the modern history of genetics began in the middle of our century, in the 1950s, with the identification of the way in which chromosomes are transmitted and the discovery of the molecular structure of DNA. The following years were marked by the progressive, patient study of the way in which the hereditary 'message' contained in DNA in the form of a succession of genes could be transmitted in protein. However, this was still a matter of getting to know the process as it takes place in nature without interfering with it.

'Manipulation' marks the last stage of the progress in genetics. Around twenty years have passed – the first work of this sort was done in 1973 – since scientists perfected a technique for introducing a fragment of extraneous DNA obtained through chemical synthesis into the hereditary patrimony of a cell. The technical term for this is DNA recombination. Molecules of DNA constructed outside the living cells are involved; these are joined to segments of DNA in order to make them replicate in a living cell.

To control the key by which hereditary characteristics are transmitted involves being able to dissolve the DNA chain and reconstruct it at will. A great variety of applications have seemed to be possible: crossing various plants and indeed vegetable and animal cells; the creation of new species of vegetables and fruits with modified characteristics; the creation of transgenic animals in the laboratory – so to speak 'custom made' – to make available experimental models for research and observation *in vitro* of the mechanisms of particular pathologies with a genetic basis, and finally the creation in the sphere of therapeutic diagnosis of organic substances – like interferon and the growth hormone – and therapeutic interventions through which genes are transferred between various organisms to correct, activate or deactivate a defective gene or to insert a defective gene so that its code can be transmitted correctly.

However, along with the promises which make genetic engineering seem to be the Eldorado of the technological age, doubts very soon arose about the safety of these interventions. The first alarm was sounded by the scientists actually involved in genetic engineering. In July 1974 a group of specialists wrote an open letter calling for self-regulation, and a moratorium put experiments in genetic modification of organisms into cold storage. However, at a conference in Asilomar in California, held in 1975, it was decided to resume work. The regulations and the precautionary measures imposed by governments have led to a stop-go progress: restrictions and strict controls have been followed by permissive sweeteners.

Adriano Bompiani has drawn a detailed map of the international regulations on genetics and biotechnology developed by supranational organizations (the Council of Europe and the UNESCO International Committee of Bioethics).[1] The results are generally disappointing: while there are emphatic reaffirmations of principles (like human dignity, freedom of research, inter-personal solidarity), no generalizable conclusions have been reached which could be translated into precise legislative norms. The impression outlined by Bompiani is that 'the continuing fragmented and sterile discussion carried on by a variety of organizations simply favours the maintaining of the "status quo", which favours uncontrolled scientific research' (133).

A new phase of the appeal to ethics in the sphere of genetics began in the spring of 1997 with the news that a mammal had been cloned from a differentiated cell from an adult (the sheep Dolly), obtained from the laboratories of the Roslin Institute in Edinburgh (the news appeared in *Nature*, 27 February 1997). The world-wide publicity for the event was encouraged by the hypothesis of the application of the same technology to human beings, at this point to produce 'custom-made human beings'.[2] The generalized reaction both from religious authorities – like the intervention of the Catholic magisterium in the person of Pope John Paul II – and from political and secular authorities – like the US president Bill Clinton, who set up a commission to investigate the ethical nature of these procedures and announced a moratorium on the public financing of research into human cloning – was one of condemnation. In this phase ethics appeared on the scene principally in the form of a broad convergence of public opinion, a mobilization of emotions and pressure for the control of scientific activity, rather than as a quest for guidelines for action supported by philosophical reflection.

II. Reflections on bioethics: continuity or novelty?

If we limit ourselves to noting the general tone of the ethical discussion which has accompanied the headlong development of genetics, whether among professional philosophers and theologians or among the wider public, we can reduce the main attitudes in the debate to two basic models: the first more centred on the novelty of the ethical problems posed by the new genetics, the second more sensitive to the continuity. Those who orientate themselves on the first model tend to emphasize the break with the past represented by the deciphering of the genetic code of living beings and the technological possibility of intervening in it. This approach tends to emphasize the consequences of the new biology: both positive (the generation of life constitutes a qualitative leap forward in the struggle against pathologies and makes it possible to model descendants at will, choosing the genetic characteristics of those to be born) and negative (reducible to the expression 'biological time bomb', which imagines consequences as catastrophic as those of the atom bomb).

By contrast, the second ideal model likes to emphasize the continuity: what is taking place in the contribution of genetic engineering is not essentially different from what humankind has known in the past. This view tends to throw cold water on the fire of both enthusiasms and preoccupations. As for the sensationalist statements, it must be noted that reality takes on a markedly different form in the world of facts. To take one example, we do not know what to do with many vegetable species which have been modified by biotechnology: what selections in the course of time will seem to correspond to our needs better than those grown naturally? In the sphere of clinical applications the intervention to which the greatest effort has been devoted, i.e. the genetic therapy of cancer (therapy in the broad sense, in that the interventions do not aim at repristinating a normal neoplastic gene function but at reinforcing existing therapies, rendering patients less sensitive to the toxicity of chemotherapy) have so far not produced the desired result. Perhaps, too, the threats connected with this technology are not as serious as was first feared. Moreover, if we maintain a historical perspective, we cannot foresee anything more tremendous than what human beings have already done without genetic engineering. Recalling the horrors that humankind has been capable of producing, we can feel justified in saying that the worst is not before us, but is rather behind us.

This summary typology of two basic orientations towards genetics proves useful above all if we conjecture that there are corresponding attitudes in ethics. The first model emphasizes the need for a new ethic which can cope with the unprecedented situation which has just been created. 'Bioethics' – a neologism which is contemporaneous with 'genetic engineering' – was proposed for the first time in 1971; it has been loudly proclaimed as an adequate response to the fact that progress in biology, and in genetics in particular, has brought us into a 'no man's land' which calls for new ethical rules. Bioethics amounts to a revoking of the mandate which society has traditionally granted to biologists and doctors to regulate their own behaviour, so that this turns into a public negotiation of ethical and legal norms.

The second attitude which we have identified tends, rather, to minimize the need for a specific ethic, tailored to the new biology. If anything, it is the usual ethics which is needed to remind everyone, in their different levels of activity, to act with a sense of responsibility.

It can be sensible and useful to be somewhat suspicious of the interest with which bioethics is promoted in various areas, as a new practice of ethical debate within society. Bioethics could be pledged to follow an ideological function, like any ideology serving camouflaged interests. Ideology offers a distorted explanation of reality, not by saying things that are intrinsically false, but by concealing the balance of power on which reality is based. Bioethics seems to support that movement which tends to direct attention towards the microcosm, towards groups, short-term relations or ultimate questions (of genetic manipulation, medically assisted techniques of reproduction and euthanasia), while leaving in the shade anything that belongs in the political and social sphere. Could what is happening in the sphere of the new biology perhaps be more usefully explored by means of questions which arise from the ethics of information (What forces does genetic technology represent? How much false information is being disseminated? In what way is the public being informed about the benefits and risks of biotechnology? How is public opinion being manipulated to achieve a consensus on mammoth projects, leaping over the element of scientific debate?), or investigting the ethics of economics (By what criteria are funds allocated to research? How are the priorities for investment established?).

However, legitimate reservations about an ideological and instrumental use of bioethics should not lead us to ignore the possibilites of a debate which emphasizes the newness rather than the continuity. Bioethics, understood in the extended sense as reflection which arises from the impact of the progress in the biological sciences and their technological applications in the environment, in medical practice and in social behaviour, can be seen as an occasion for engaging in ethical reflection.

III. New genetics and the functions of ethics

In our society there is not only a pluralism of ethical systems but also a plurality of ethical functions. In his introduction to the Italian edition of E. E. Shelp's *Bioethics and Technology*,[3] Antonio Autiero suggests three functions of ethics: control, management and legitimation. This hypothesis is confirmed by the phenomenological analysis of the appeals to ethics in the area of the new genetics. Ethics is asked to define the limits which shall not be passed; to evaluate the prices to be paid and the risks to be run in comparison with the benefits hoped for; to establish a link between the operative level and the high ideal values. Together, these three functions of ethics can offer an effective orientation in the sphere of genetic interventions into human beings.

The function of control has become a priority in the present phase of the development of genetics and the possibilities of intervening in the structure of living beings. Control, with clear lines between what can be done and what should not be allowed, should prevent the possibility of doing something from being the sole reason why it is done. The controlling function of ethics borders on the law and tends to be confused with it. This proximity is advantageous for ethics, which risks not knowing how to assert its own specific character. The moral law cannot be subject to the rule of the majority, as happens in democratic regimes. The legal norm is in turn subjected to an ethical judgment, being confronted with a higher authority than the law, for example human rights.

Despite the difficulties in arriving at a concrete delimitation of what is lawful, because there are different anthropologies, a basic consensus is being outlined in the West about the lines of defence to be drawn, protecting human beings from manipulative interventions which go against the values recognized by both religious and secular traditions. The barrier universally placed against cloning human beings is a clear example of such consensus.

In the sphere of management attributed to ethics, the contribution which ethics can make is to bring out explicitly the choices and criteria on which actions are based. Rather than making prohibitions or laying down limits which must not be passed, as ethics does in its controlling function, management requires ethics to develop norms capable of regulating an order in the wake of new practices.

Important though the criterion of responsibility is in evaluating the transition to action – as Hans Jonas has repeatedly argued, specifically in the context of the new biology[4] – there is no need to emphasize the continued urgency of being subject to the criteria of rationality. Ethics is and must remain a privileged place for the exercise of an inexorably critical reason. This scrupulous exercise of practical reason first of all requires the power to distinguish between true and false. This is not as simple a task as it might seem at first sight. This is shown by manifest errors in news spread as true which has proved later to be disinformation.

A second exercise of rationality consists in distinguishing the important from the accidental. The list of what it is possible to achieve through genetic engineering is like the 'laundry list' on which we find the most disparate articles of clothing mixed up. To choose the colour of one's child's eyes – supposing that that were technically possible – cannot be put on the same level of possibilities as preventing a serious genetic abnormality. The very choice of the sex of one's descendants, intervening in the selection of the gametes which carry the desired chromosome, does not have the same significance if it is simply the exercising of an arbitrary preference rather than an attempt to avoid the transmission of a pathology linked to sex. However, it is not as easy as it seems to draw a line between therapeutic and non-therapeutic interventions, and there are many who bear witness to the logic of the slippery slope which opens up once the principle of the improvement of nature is accepted as an object which it is ethically legitimate to pursue.

Moreover it is necessary to distinguish judgment from the emotions. Genetic engineering tends to be spoken of most often in an evocative and mythological language: the work of 'sorcerer's apprentices', a 'biological time-bomb', the creation of superman and chimpanzee man, the production of monsters. This is a language which is usually intimidating, intended to provoke strong emotions – which tend to welcome research when there is hope or to condemn genetic engineering *en bloc* when fear predominates – rather than critical reflection. In the face of such frames of mind the 'management' function of ethics is destined to come to grief.

The third function of ethics – which I have called legitimation – here serves to relate basic genetic knowledge and the applications of bio-engineering to the loftiest human ideals. There is a general consensus over the high moral value of therapy. The possibility of correcting a genetic defect by inserting into the genome of an individual a healthy copy of the defective gene has opened up a new ethic in the history of medicine. There is a general agreement, expressed by official documents of ethical commissions and legislative regulations, that such interventions should be limited – at least provisionally – to somatic cells, excluding germ line cells (a modification of this type of genome would transmit the alteration to progeny). The motives for exclusion are prudential by nature: these interventions do not have a sufficiently solid experimental base to justify their application to human beings. However, germ line human genetic therapy cannot be ruled out in principle.[5]

As for the legitimation of interventions of genetic engineering which aim at improving human nature, here we are moving in the sphere of that aspiration to the good which is the essential character of being, along with the true and the beautiful. Thus here we are in a region in which metaphysical and religious aspirations meet. In such a quest for the 'good life' we can identify a fundamental dimension of human existence with which the new genetics must be confronted. It must be concerned to safeguard personal values, or to guarantee to each person the capacity to have self-esteem. An essential condition for this is that each human being should be given a personal value without other qualifications, simply on the basis of belonging to the human species. That prevents anyone from being able to claim to pass judgment and to decide to whom human rights apply. People are not co-opted as members of human society on the basis of particular determining factors, although everyone comes under the force of a particular law. The new biology must keep an eye on this condition, which we can call 'the prohibition of a definition'.

Those who are found lacking in respect of the criteria assumed by culture as ideal must be safeguarded through the virtues of *pietas* and *sollicitudo*, respect and care. This is a very familiar perspective in the prophetic vision of the man who stands at the beginning of Christianity, for whom it was the stone rejected by the builders which became the headstone of the corner (cf. Matt. 21.42).

Translated by John Bowden

Notes

1. A. Bompiani, E. Brovedani and C. Cirotto, *Nuova genetica, nove responsabilità*, Cinisello 1997.

2. J. Harris, *Wonderwoman and Superman*, Oxford 1992.

3. A. Autiero, preface to the Italian edition of E. E. Shelp (ed.), *Theology and Bioethics*, Dordrecht 1985 (*Teologia e Bioetica*, Bologna 1989).

4. H. Jonas, *The Imperative of Responsibility*, Chicago 1984.

5. R. Muson and L. H. Davis, 'Germ-line Gene Therapy and the Medical Imperative', in *Kennedy Institute of Ethics Journal* 2, 1992, 2, 1357–68.

II · Intervention before Birth

Ethical Questions in Genetic Counselling: How Far Do Concepts like 'Non-Directivity' and 'Ethical Neutrality' Help in Solving Problems?

Stella Reiter-Theil

Introduction

Ethical problems in genetic counselling need an explicit ethical analysis. However, there is often an attempt to solve them only pragmatically, by means of the technical concepts of counselling. This approach fails to provide fundamental reflection on ethical questions and conflicts between the different aims and interests of those concerned, and limits the communicative possibilities of working out solutions to problems in co-operation with those involved. Here rules like non-directivity and neutrality play a prominent role in counselling. I shall go on to analyse these and discuss them against the background of the context of their origin in psychotherapy, and investigate whether they can be transferred to genetic counselling practically and ethically.

I. The problem: implicit or explicit ethics?

Case study

'Huntington's chorea, a form of St Vitus' dance which atrophies the brain and after a series of progressive changes finally results in a major degree of dementia, was diagnosed in a thirty-eight-year-old male. The woman doctor involved in genetic counselling explains to the patient, who has three younger brothers and sisters, that this hereditary disease usually manifests itself between the ages of thirty-five and fifty and could also develop in any of them. The patient refuses to allow this diagnosis to be passed on to his brothers and sisters' (this case study appears in Kahlke 1995, 60).

This raises a number of ethical questions and problems for the doctor. Does the patient have the right to keep to himself his knowledge of the risk to which his brothers and sisters are exposed? Is the doctor perhaps – despite the patient's refusal – obliged to inform the other members of the family once her attempts to convince the patient have failed? Can she invite the brothers and sisters of the patient to undergo a family genetic investigation without giving any details? Or would a better solution be to inform the patient's own doctor of the diagnosis – again against the patient's declared will – and leave further action to him? What responsibility does the doctor have, given that the brothers and sisters of the patient – like the patient himself – want to have children soon who will also genetically be at risk of falling ill with Huntington's chorea as adults?

This case study is sufficient to illustrate the wealth of ethical questions with which counsellors and counselled are confronted in genetic counselling. At the same time it can be seen that these questions challenge current concepts like 'non-directivity' or 'neutrality' in the role of the counsellor.

After a long period in which the concept of non-directivity was a central point of reference for the role of the genetic counsellor (Wertz et al. 1988, 1990), doubts are increasingly arising as to whether this rule in counselling technique is in fact appropriate (Clark 1991, Wolff and Jung 1994; Yarborough et al. 1989; Reiter-Theil 1995). Criticism of it begins at a variety of points.

1. The concept of non-directivity has not been worked out sufficiently for genetic counselling and is difficult to translate because of its vagueness and contradictoriness.

2. A non-directive attitude takes too little account of the obligation of the counsellor to help the one seeking advice.

3. The widespread appeal to the rule of non-directivity represents a more or less conscious attempt to answer unexplained questions of ethical orientation in genetic counselling with the help of a 'technical' rule.

It follows from these three points of criticism that a further discussion of ethical and practical problems of genetic counselling is called for, and that is what this article will attempt. The aim is to make a contribution to explicit ethical reflection.

II. Non-directivity in psychotherapy – the context of its origin and its ethical significance

If we are to be able to judge what significance the concept of so-called non-directivity is to have in genetic counselling, we need to clarify the theoretical and practical goals in the light of which this 'technical', but also implicitly ethical rule, was introduced. So-called humanistic psychotherapy, which comprises numerous orientations like the client-centred psychotherapy founded by Rogers (including conversational psychotherapy), gestalt psychotherapy, transactional analysis and many others, has been called the 'third force in psychotherapy' (Quitmann 1985) – over against classical psychoanalysis and behaviourism.

So-called non-directivity is one of the three fundamental rules on which Rogers based his orientation, which was then new. It is inseparably bound up with the second rule, that of the authenticity of the therapist or counsellor (which is also called personal congruity or authenticity), and the third rule, that of the need for positive evaluation, acceptance, emotional warmth in the therapist's basic attitude towards the client. There are tensions or conflicts in this triad of rules, which the practitioner has to learn to deal with by particular procedures. Tensions can develop in particular between the client's requirement for warmth and acceptance and the simultaneous requirement for authenticity on the part of the therapist. Every therapist or counsellor knows that it is not always possible to accept clients or patients emotionally. How much authenticity is then correct or therapeutic? A further source of tensions and conflict which is important for the question with which we are concerned is the relationship between the rule of authenticity and non-directivity. To be non-directive means not to want to give any direction to the patient, at least in a manner which would limit this other in finding his or her own way.

III. The transference of non-directivity to genetic counselling

1. Motives for transference

Can this rule be grounded in the context of genetic counselling or transferred to it (Schmidtke and Wolff 1991)? What interest is attached to an appeal to this concept? Should a barrier be erected against the dominance – or the charge of dominance – of the experts, who in genetic counselling could possibly claim not only medical but also moral competence? It is hoped that the adoption of a non-directive attitude will protect the counsellor against the temptation to meet the client's desire for help in making a decision, indeed in the decision itself? What part is played by the problematic role which genetics has had in Germany and also in other countries, in connection with the crimes aginst humanity committed by the National Socialists in the sphere of eugenics and racism (Tröhler, Reiter-Theil 1997)?

These reasons for an orientation on non-directivity, which all have some plausibility, suggest that here the issue is not just practical and methodological aspects in the sense of the technique of counselling. The orientation on non-directivity as a 'technical' guideline for the counsellor's basic

attitude has numerous ethical implications which the term brings with it as it were incidentally. The disadvantage here is that merely implicit, i.e. unexpressed, ethical significances of the term make no contribution
• to focused ethical reflection on the problems of counselling,
• to criticism,
• to the foundation of ethical judgments or
• to the resolution of conflicts.

2. *Ethical implications*

What ethical significance does the orientation on the concept of non-directivity have in genetic counselling? Here the aspect of restraint appears most clearly: a non-directive counsellor is concerned not to intervene in the decisions of the person seeking advice, and not even to influence him or her. Put positively, this corresponds to respect for the self-determination of the client. At the same time, this restraint contains inbuilt protection from possibly wrong judgment or decisions on the part of the counsellor, which could take place if he or she were to depart from the non-directive line. In ethical terms, this amounts to a criterion for avoiding damage which the person seeking advice from the counselling might possibly incur. More indirectly, one can also discern the motive of providing counselling in the best interest of the client. This presupposes that uninfluenced, free decisions on the part of the client are the best to put into practice and live out, whereas decisions which were not made freely could in some circumstances be associated with any subsequent difficulties that the client might experience. In ethical terms, this would amount to an interest in acting for the well-being of the client. However, paradoxically, precisely this orientation, once identified, usually seems to be associated with the opposite attitude, which is active or directive.

But in the context of genetic counselling it may be difficult to define the specific nature of the 'well-being' of those involved and directly or indirectly affected by decisions; indeed perhaps this should not be expected of the counsellor at all. In my view, well-being can only be considered or reconstructed and lived through retrospectively by those involved. And it is precisely here that the origin and basis of the rule of non-directivity lie: because counsellors are aware of their limitations in knowing what will later prove best for their clients, they should be cautious about intervening or influencing. Those involved therefore cannot be relieved in advance of the task of evaluating, choosing or deciding about what is to come; this does not belong within the 'technical' or professional competence of the genetic counsellor in the narrower sense, at least not under the aspect of non- directivity.

3. Counter-arguments

However, the experience that quite often non-directivity is found to be inadequate in practice, even in psychological and psychotherapeutic counselling (from which the rule was 'derived'), tells against all too optimistic a transference of it to medical contexts, in this case to genetic counselling. Its inadequacy can already be seen in problems of relationship, conflicts in the family, difficulties over upbringing or sexual malfunction, where in contrast to medicine the issue is seldom one of life or death but usually of quality of life, life-style and goals in life. The explicit desire of clients for help in deciding, for a new direction which leads out of their dead end, indeed for values which they would not have arrived at by themselves, is not taken seriously enough by counsellors who proceed all too strictly in accordance with the rule of non-directivity. This tendency towards deliberate frustration of the client's desire for orientation or support has become evident after the results of a catamnestic investigation, especially among counsellors who have been introduced more superficially into the 'technical team' without the relevant further training (Reiter-Theil et al. 1985a, 1985b). This finding may also be of relevance for planning the further training of genetic counsellors to improve their psycho-social and ethical competence.

The arguments against a simple transference of the rule of non-directivity to genetic counselling can be further sharpened by pointing out that genetic counselling – in contrast to most cases of psychological or psychotherapeutic counselling – essentially consists in the communication of information (Reif and Baitsch 1986), whereas in psychological or psychotherapeutic counselling, characteristically the aim is to encourage new possibilities within the psyche or personal relationship, i.e. new perspectives and competences which are not derived from quantitative, empirical data that can be checked out. By its very nature, the communication of information involves presenting new facts and interconnections on a professional basis, correcting errors or false assumptions on the part of the client. Therefore a rule like non-directivity cannot find any application in the components of genetic counselling which are related to the communication of information. Far less can the information relevant in this context, say about a genetic risk along with all the consequences for action that it entails, be 'neutral' (emotionally or morally) for the members of the family concerned. The context and the manner of explanation already determine essential aspects of the non-neutrality of individual units of information. The same considerations, possibilities and limitations of a neutral attitude like that in psychological or psychotherapeutic counselling also apply to a further component of genetic counselling in which the aim is to help the client to make a good and responsible decision (Reiter-Theil 1988, 1989, 1993). In connection with these elements in helping the client to make a decision it is desirable for a transfer to be made from psychological counselling, including empirical evaluation, to the forming of the concepts and practice of genetic counselling. Genetic counselling should have three supports: genetic, psycho-social and ethical competence.

IV. Constellations of ethical reflection and communication in counselling

In assessing the question of the neutrality of the counsellor, it is important to distinguish different constellations of ethical awareness in the two parties involved in the counselling. Essentially, four constellations can emerge here. In the first constellation, both sides agree that at the point of counselling or working out a decision, no specifically ethical question is being discussed. This agreement may come about tacitly or even unconsciously. A further constellation in which counsellors and clients or patients are agreed then forms if both share the view that the content of the counselling and options for possible action have important ethical implications; here opinions can diverge as to whether these can and should be discussed in the counselling. However, the agreement about the presence of ethical problems or even the need to work on these does not necessarily also mean agreement on the assessment and evaluation of the ethical questions. In the case of ethical dissent, the discussion of these topics will have to be managed with special sensitivity and tact by the counsellor. A constellation of clear disunity comes about if either the counsellor sees an ethical problem which the client does not, or vice versa. In the latter case the counsellor can attempt to help the client to understand and solve his or her ethical problem. If the counsellor has ethical problems with the desires or behaviour of the client, this possibility does not exist. It can then be better if the counsellor gives up the case or transfers it to a colleague with competence in ethics. This constellation of disagreement may be one of the most serious challenges to genetic counselling, and raises both the question of neutrality and that of identity in the role of the counsellor.

V. (How) Can ethical questions be discussed in counselling?

Whether and in what circumstances a counsellor should talk with clients or patients about the ethical dimension of genetic counselling and the options which arise cannot be answered with a simple 'yes' or 'no'. Two milder variants are conceivable between these two radical positions: 'no, but', and 'yes, but'. These positions are listed in Table 1, together with the reasons or risks:

Table 1		
Talking with Clients about Ethics		
Position	Reasons	Risks
1. No, never!	Respect for autonomy; privacy of patient; value-free medicine	Neglect, nihilism
2. Yes, always!	Ethics cannot be separated from health-care professions; identity; transparency.	Moralizing, paternalism
3. No, except in cases where the integrity of the counsellor is threatened	Self-protection of the counsellor, identity; see 1.	See 1. and 2.
4. Yes, except in cases where client(s) refuse(s) to	See 1. and 2; chance for better decisions	Expecting too much from client(s)

The first position can be regarded as a radical liberal approach, which does not intervene in the patient's self-determination or private sphere, even by asking about his or her wishes and preferences. The risks in such an attitude lie in the possibility of overlooking or neglecting an important ethical problem, which would therefore not be treated and resolved in the patient's best interests. In genetic counselling, such an approach can encourage tendencies towards a therapeutic ethical nihilism or at least provoke criticism to this effect from outside. In the human sciences, an increasing readiness can be noted to question the concept of value-free science. In medicine the situation seems to be more ambiguous: a considerable part of medical practice is still characterized by an attempt to exclude values and ethics, at least in direct contact with the patient. However, the Hippocratic medical tradition, and also modern medicine with its lively ethical discussion, tends more to support the view that the healing professions as a whole should not be looked at apart from their inherent ethical dimension. Consequently this position can be justified to the patient with values like transparency, openness and honesty, and also the need for the counsellors to preserve their own professional identity.

However, this approach entails the risk of a moralizing of the medical services. There is also a risk of creating an atmosphere of medical or moral paternalism if this approach is associated with a claim on the part of the counsellor to moral authority, coupled with a medical and professional superiority on the basis of greater knowledge.

The third position can be characterized as a more defensive attitude: only if the counsellor feels that his or her values are affected by the ethical implications or consequences of the process of counselling should the discussion of these ethical questions with the client be engaged in. The reasons for this position correspond to those in position 1; the risks correspond to those in positions 1 and 2.

The fourth and last position represents a milder variant of position 2 and means that the discussion of ethical aspects of the counselling or treatment are part of the practice of medicine and the healing professions, but should not be engaged in without the agreement of the patient or client. The reasons for this approach, which correspond to those for positions 1 and 2, include the aim of creating a better basis for the decisions which have to be made by the client. The danger in this position is that it asks too much of clients and patients; however, the risk of moralizing or a paternalistic domination seems slight, in so far as the client's possible reluctance to discuss ethical questions is respected. All in all this position has the best basis of the four possible positions.

VI. A differentiated model of 'neutrality' for counselling

The acceptance of the rule of non-directivity, the attempts to avoid medical paternalism and above all the concern not to moralize the wishes of patients in counselling and treatment have contributed to a rhetoric of neutrality in which this is singled out as an ideal, respectful and generally superior basic attitude (Reiter-Theil 1989). On the basis of the analysis of constellations for ethical reflection and communication and the various options as to whether or not to discuss the ethical dimension of counselling with clients, there is no doubt that ethical neutrality cannot represent a simple solution. Several levels must be distinguished and noted in assessing the significance of neutrality in counselling. Table 2 sums up the proposals for assessing neutrality; these derive from investigations which have been published elsewhere (Reiter-Theil 1989, 1995, 1997):

Table 2

Ethical Orientation in the Counsellor's Role: The Problem of 'Neutrality' at Different Levels

1. Relation between counsellor and client(s): *no neutrality*, because accepting, warm attitude towards client(s) is necessary.

2. Professional identity of counsellor: *no neutrality*, because of the goals of health care, and because ethical principles, codes, guidelines, etc. are binding.

3. Personal identity of counsellor: *no neutrality*, because personal values and goals set limits to acting in a 'neutral' way – authenticity instead.

4. Personal values of client(s): *'technical neutrality'*, because of respect for autonomy and privacy of client(s), but explicit reflection of possible consequences of choices.

5. Conflicts of interests on the side of client(s): *'technical neutrality'*, because of respect for autonomy, empathy, and fairness for everyone involved by explicit reflection of possible consequences of decisions.

6. Difficulties with 'technical neutrality' towards client(s): *reflection, supervision, transferral*, in order to avoid maleficence, judgmental response, or manipulation.

At levels 1–3, no neutrality is possible in the counsellor's role, because here non-neutral value-orientated attitudes are called for, like an accepting, warm basic attitude, orientation on aims, principles or codes; and aspects of the personal identity and authenticity of the counsellor are addressed. These levels include the person of the counsellor and his or her relationship to the client to a greater degree than the following levels (4 and 5). At these levels, where the focus is on the client's perspective, a so-called technical neutrality is necessary in order to make the professional detachment of the counsellor possible and to guarantee protection of the private sphere and respect for the client. If difficulties with the counsellor's technical neutrality emerge, a reflective attitude is indicated, which should make a new orientation in the role of the counsellor or in the relationship with the client easier.

Here we are confronted with a mixture of implicit and explicit ethical concepts which enter the professional and ethical orientation of counselling. The core ethical principles – each time related to levels 1 to 6 – are: 1. the obligation to help, and respect for the autonomy of the client; 2. a general orientation on the ethical basis of the profession; 3. personal ethical (or moral) identity; 4. respect for the private sphere and self-determination of the client and concern for the consequences of the action; 5. respect for autonomy, empathy and fairness for all those concerned, and respect for the consequences of the action; 6. the obligation to avoid damage and to refrain from manipulation and moral condemnation. The four principles worked out by Beauchamp and Childress (1989) – respect for autonomy, avoiding damage, offering help and fairness – are included here but are inadequate; therefore we have worked out two further components of ethical orientation: (a) a general orientation on the ethical basis of the healing professions, and (b) a personal ethical identity. There is a close connection between these two components, since professional guidelines can support the identity of those engaged in healing professions; but there is also a potential of conflict which arises when personal values diverge from professional ethical standards.

To all appearances this dimension has so far been neglected in current medical ethics. Professional counselling – like any other professional activity – has a normative basis and inherent general ethical principles; these need to be recognized. On the other hand, counsellors can act ethically and professionally only if they remain true to themselves and act in accord with their personal ethical identity. In this formulation the tension between objectivism and subjectivism or between generalism and individualism becomes obvious. As with the neutrality of the counsellor, here too there is no option to choose one or the other; rather, we must formulate specific answers to specific challenges which nevertheless follow general lines of ethical orientation. The more ethical concepts are made explicit and the more we are aware of them, the better our answers to the questions will be.

VII. Answers to questions – back to the case study

In our case study we do not discover anything about the way in which the doctor who counsels has talked with the client about the ethical problems which arise from his desire to keep quiet about the diagnosis and the genetic risks. Despite – or because of? – the official non-directivity in genetic counselling which is widespread in Germany, several steps are considered which, while they are not in accord with the wishes of the patient and are not discussed with him, nevertheless are meant to solve the problem of explaining the situation of genetic risk to his brothers and sisters independently. Here it would seem ethically appropriate to make one more attempt in conversation with the client to impress on him that an open discussion of the ethical questions, and especially of his responsibility towards the interests of other members of his family, is necessary. Here it can be of decisive importance to discover why he is against passing on the diagnosis and the consequences for his relatives associated with it, and to attempt to remove these problems. If no agreement can be achieved by this means, ethical counselling with an experienced colleague should follow. If all these possibilities fail, the client should be informed if information is to be passed on to relatives against his will so that in the circumstances he can still consider some form of co-operation 'to save face'.

The steps contain clear ethical positions which are incompatible with a 'neutral attitude'; on the other hand, in arguing with the motives of the client in withholding information, in discussing his anxieties and wishes, technical 'neutrality' and active rejection of moralizing is a guideline, in that the client must be shown respect and understanding – even if the counsellor does not agree with his conclusions or decisions. This also applies to the emergence of conflicts of interest between members of the family, in which a competent counsellor must preserve openness and show respect, understanding and fairness to all sides, even if he or she feels closer to the concern of one 'party'. These technical aspects which survive from an undifferentiated 'neutrality' on the part of the adviser which is all too often called for – restraint along with the elements of a positive ethical orientation – should make it possible for the counsellor to perceive ethical problems realistically and to solve them in an appropriate way by recognizing the ethical framework of his or her action and as far as possible clarifying the ethical dimension of the situation with the client.

Translated by John Bowden

Bibliography

T. L. Beauchamp and J. F. Childress (1989), *Principles of Medical Ethics*, New York.

A. Clark (1991), 'Is non-directive genetic counselling possible?', *Lancet* II: 998–1001.

A. P. Goldstein (1978), *Strukturierte Lerntherapie. Ansätze zu einer Psychotherapie der sozial Benachteiligten*, Munich.

W. Kahlke (1995), 'Eugenik', in W. Kahlke and S. Reiter-Theil (eds), *Ethik in der Medizin*, Stuttgart, 55–67.

H. Quitmann (1985), *Humanistische Psychologie*, Göttingen.

M. Reif and H. Baitsch (1986), *Genetische Beratung*, Berlin.

S. Reiter-Theil, L. Reiter, E. Steiner and M. Much (1985a), 'Einstellungen von Klienten zur Eheberatung und Beratungserfolg. Eine katamnestische Untersuchung. Teil I: Erwartungen, Zufriedenheit und Enttäuschung in der Eheberatung', *Familiendynamik* 10, 147–57.

——(1985b), 'Einstellungen von Klienten zur Eheberatung und Beratungserfolg. Eine katamnestische Untersuchung. Teil 2: Veränderungen nach der Eheberatung im Erleben der Klienten', *Familiendynamik* 10, 157–69.

S. Reiter-Theil (1988), *Autonomie und Gerechtigkeit. Das Beispiel der Familientherapie für eine therapeutische Ethik*, Berlin, Heidelberg, New York.

——(1989), 'Therapeutische Neutralität in der Paar- und Sexualtherapie', *Ethik Med* 1, 99–107.

——(1993), 'Wertfreiheit, Abstinenz und Neutralität? Normative Aspekte in Psychoanalyse und Familientherapie', in L. H. Eckensberger and U. Gahde (eds), *Ethische Norm und empirische Hypothese. Beiträge zum Forschungsschwerpunkt Ethik – interdisziplinärer Ethikdiskurs der Deutschen Forschungsgemeinschaft*, Frankfurt am Main, 302–27.

——(1995), 'Nichtdirektivität und Ethik in der genetischen Beratung', in F. Ratz (ed.), *Zwischen Neutralität und Weisung – zur Theorie und Praxis von Beratung in der Humangenetik*, Munich, 83–91.

——(1997), 'Ethical Neutrality in Counselling? The Challenge of Infertility', in D. Mieth and E. Hildt (eds), *In Vitro Fertilization in the 90's – Towards a Medical, Social and Ethical Evaluation of IVF*, Hampshire.

C. R. Rogers (1972), *Die nichtdirektive Beratung*, Munich.

J. Schmidtke and G. Wolff (1991), 'Die "Altersindikation", ihre Abschaffung und die Folgen', *Med. Genetik* 1, 16–19.

T. Schroeder-Kurth (1989), 'Indikationen für die genetische Familienberatung', *Ethik Med.* 1, 195–205.

U. Tröhler and S. Reiter-Theil (eds), *Ethische Kodizes in Medizin und Biotechnologie 1947–1997. Auftrag für die Zukunft*, Göttingen.

D. C. Wertz and J. C. Fletcher (1988), 'Attitudes of Genetic Counselors: A Multinational Survey', *Am J Hum Genet* 42, 592–600.

——and J. J. Mulvihill (1990), 'Medical Geneticists Confront Ethical Dilemmas: Cross-cultural Comparisons among 18 Nations', *Am J Hum Genet* 46, 1200–13.

G. Wolff and C. Juntt (1994), 'Nichtdirektivität und genetische Beratung', *Med Genet* 6, 195–204.

M. Yarborough, J. A. Scott and L. K. Dixon (1989), 'The Role of Beneficence in Clinical Genetics: Non-directive Counseling Reconsidered', *Theoretical Medicine* 10, 139–49.

Genetic Counselling: Parental Autonomy or Acceptance of Limits?[1]

Liz Hepburn

Modern clinical geneticists have stressed that their intervention is a service, that pre-natal counselling is non-directive and that they seek only to support clients in making informed reproductive choices.[2] Of course, the anguish of prospective parents at risk of having children with genetic abnormalities deserves sympathetic support and assistance. Nevertheless, the most common response to a serious genetic pre-natal diagnosis is abortion,[3] and one cannot help wondering whether the very provision of the service does not predispose all involved to selective termination of pregnancy. A corollary of this is whether our practices in this field represent a radical rejection of the limits of being human, as has been suggested by Stephen Post,[4] and a quest for control over contingency.

At present pre-natal genetic testing and counselling is largely restricted to groups at special risk. However, Bosk[5] asks what sort of society might see routine genetic counselling as an appropriate means to health care:

> Is genetic counselling the kind of ceremony that one would expect in a society where the cult of the individual prevailed and the collective conscience was diffuse, attenuated, and abstract? . . . Is genetic counselling the form that help and care take in a society dominated by a spirit of calculation?

One is also prompted to ask whether genetic investigation is driven by therapeutic concerns or commercial interests. The parallel with the pharmaceutical industry is obvious.[6] What I wish to do is to explore some of these questions in terms of what we seem to be saying about what it is to be human and the kind of future we would like to imagine for ourselves.

Case study

Jenny Dobson is a young married woman with no children of her own. Ten years ago she graduated as a nurse and practised in various settings before deciding to specialize in perinatal nursing. In intensive care nurseries she became more and more interested in congenital abnormalities and saw in the new genetic tests a potential means for alleviating suffering both for children and parents. Preventing the birth of those with gravely debilitating genetic disorders seemed to her to be an appropriate new way of serving the goals of medicine and nursing – a new form of care which alleviated suffering. Jenny studied part-time and became a genetic counsellor working in both Catholic and state-run hospital clinics. As she had anticipated, the range of genetic tests expanded quite rapidly and the service was always fully booked.

When Jenny came to see me she was troubled by several aspects of her own practice and what she foresaw as likely developments in the field of genetic counselling. Basically, her questions centred upon issues of choice, autonomy, definitions of normality and the appropriate goals of medicine. Although her training had emphasized the importance of value-neutrality in the clinical setting, she had begun to feel uneasy about new questions asked by prospective parents, questions which blurred the distinction between pathological abnormality and minor disability. In the face of new demands that genetic testing be used to select for desirable characteristics was 'value-neutrality' an ethically tenable stance? Could she any longer practise as if deference to a narrowly conceived notion of patient autonomy was the only ethical consideration? Were there any objective ways to differentiate disability and desirability?

What had brought these issues into sharp relief for Jenny was – admittedly an extreme case – an approach by a deaf couple who regard deafness as superior to hearing. They claimed that hearing is a burdensome condition and so they wished selectively to abort any non-deaf child. In giving priority to the principle of autonomy, by supporting the parents in their decision, Jenny felt she would compromise the integrity of her practice within a health-care framework.

Genetic counselling: in whose best interests?

The very provision of the service suggests that foreknowledge of a genetic disability permits better decision-making on the part of the potential parents. Most often, the decision will be to take evasive action. In the case of some Ashkenazy Jewish communities most affected by Tay Sachs disease, the information is provided to adolescents, and carriers can then elect not to marry other carriers. More recently, IVF procedures have been employed, so that only unaffected offspring are transferred to the mother's uterus and embryos carrying the genetic disease are discarded. Genetic tests conducted during pregnancy give the expectant parents the option of selective abortion. So, ought we to select offspring using genetic data?

The issue of protection is important. Although the developing child may be investigated, it seems that a poor prognosis is not always handled therapeutically. There is a lack of symmetry here. The psychological health of the parents is protected and death is sometimes evaluated as in the child's best interests. In shaping the future, we need to consider how we can best discharge our responsibilities to those not yet born – for 'The non-existent has no lobby, and the unborn are powerless'.[7]

Confusion as to who the patient is abounds. Investigations of the foetus at the request of the parent raise issues about disclosure of information. If modern practice separates mother and child and provides separate regimes of treatment and care, then perhaps it is an inappropriate invasion of the privacy of the developing child to conduct genetic tests on him/her. Further, as Steel has said,[8] testing may shift the focus of attention from the person to the disability and perhaps from treatment to prevention. Treatment by two physicians, an obstetrician and a foetologist, sets the scene for radical disruption of what we have thought of as the most intimate of human relationships. If one physician must act in the interests of the child and the other for the mother, we must ask whether we can any longer use the parent-child relationship as the archetype of responsibility.[9] The further question of when to disclose information to the child is also problematic, for the information may be a burden or a boon.[10]

For Jenny, it often seems that only the expressed interests of the prospective parents are considered. More and more she sees couples for whom the prospect of any abnormality in the developing child is problematic. Focus on the interests of the parents as clients requires that the interests of the child-to-be and of those already amongst us and carrying the particular disability are sidelined. What seems to be happening is that an urge to alleviate suffering is gradually being transformed into a demand that abnormality be eliminated, and in the case confronting Jenny, that specific characteristics be sought. In this she sees a subtle distortion of the aims of medicine and of medical ethics.

The quest for perfection

In conventional medical practice, people are advised to avoid certain practices which are hazardous to health. In this we have implicitly judged that some states of being are preferable to others. The concept of health involves normative judgments that some human characteristics, although perhaps common, are not desirable. We hold that care of one's health is a duty, though the concept of health itself is something of an enigma.[11] Hence it is claimed that genetic counselling is just an extension of a set of practices in medicine and public health which are not only acceptable but desirable.

Proponents of genetic counselling see it as permitting people to make informed choices about bringing to birth children whose health can never be good. This seems utterly consistent with the precepts of health-care practice. The fact that parents seek the information in the first place suggests that the service is seen as valuable. However, the most frequent response to a poor prognosis is selective abortion. Of course, this is not the only possible response, and foreknowledge may assist prospective parents to access support groups and prepare better for the birth of a disabled child.

Central to the claim that genetic counselling is a form of disease prevention is the characterization of genetic abnormality as genetic disease. The success of modern medicine has led us to believe that we will finally eradicate disease. The difficulty is of course, that eradicating a disease caused by an external agent can be achieved by eliminating the agent, but genetic disease is, at present, largely dealt with by eliminating the carrier. For those who hold that human life begins at conception this requires the killing of a living, human being. Thus genetic counselling, linked with therapeutic genetic engineering techniques or simply as preparation for coping with a disabled child, is the only approach acceptable to those who view human life as worthy of protection from conception onwards.

Of course, this creates a good deal of tension for Jenny. For half her working week she communicates her diagnoses in strictly clinical and objective terms. In fact, prospective parents using this service must indicate a readiness to undergo selective abortion if a particular diagnosis is deemed to indicate gross and irreparable abnormality. Her time in the Catholic hospital, by contrast, is predicated on the view that pregnancy must be supported to the point of viability, unless the continuation of the pregnancy threatens the life of the mother.

Further pressure is created, though, when selective abortion is approved for even minor abnormalities. Jenny is concerned that as genetic tests become routine, her practice will become a quest for perfection rather than an effort to eliminate genetic disease. The acceptability of abortion as a response to even moderate disability means that the way in which she communicates her diagnosis is critical to the decision. It is clear to Jenny that her clinical practice is in fact, value laden, not value neutral. The request from the deaf couple, although perhaps understandable, requires Jenny to redefine the parameters of her practice and to accept that her definitions of health and disease are necessarily subjective.

Disease, disability and unacceptability

The most common criticism of pre-natal genetic counselling[12] is that the purpose is to identify risk so as to take remedial or evasive action. Identifying certain human characteristics, with a view to ensuring that they are not expressed, requires that we count some genetic abnormalities as unacceptable. In this case, genetic testing is used to select future progeny on eugenic lines. The response of organizations representing disabled people in Germany and the Netherlands to genetic counselling has been to claim a 'right to abnormality', arguing that the resulting diversity is a challenge which may become a strength for a community.[13]

Assessments as to which embryo shall live require us to say what counts, what makes life worth living. In some cases, the affected individual may not be aware of her abnormality; for her, life may seem fine. If that is the case, then the decision that her life is not worth living is made in the interests of her carers. Even if the child with a debilitating condition is fully aware, as Alison Davis has pointed out so eloquently, to permit anyone to decide that the lives of disabled people are not worth living allows us to say that we may extinguish human life for the convenience of another person.[14] The practice of genetic testing and counselling may reinforce this attitude.

Numerous commentators stress that selective implantation or abortion ought to be restricted to serious disabilities such as Down's syndrome or cystic fibrosis.[15] Still, people like Alison Davis and Diana Sanderson[16] claim that life can be worth living even with spina bifida, and certainly the prognosis for cystic fibrosis is improving as new approaches to treatment develop. But these new approaches will only be pursued if there are significant numbers of people living with cystic fibrosis. In fact, the prospect of the elimination of a disease by genetic selection may divert clinicians and research from those conditions and prove a distinct disadvantage to those affected now, or in the future.

Evaluating the gravity of specific conditions will always be fraught with difficulty. The point that both Davis and Sanderson make is that these decisions ought not be left to the able-bodied. The provision of genetic testing and counselling services gives one class of people extraordinary power over the lives of another class of people. It is just this which is disturbing Jenny in her clinical work. Paradoxically, we seem prepared to eliminate the very people before birth whom anti-discrimination legislation seeks to protect after birth.

Risk, uncertainty and moral decision-making

The truth that we are much more than our genes becomes a crucial issue within the field of genetic counselling. Most of the advice which genetic counsellors can give will be in the form of probabilities. They speak about the chance of bearing an affected child as well as the likelihood of the problem being severe. Thus, decisions based on complex data must be taken at a time of emotional lability and the nature of the best advice available often seems equivocal.[17]

Given that the vast majority of predispositions which new genetic tests may identify are multifactorial, the value of the information is at least questionable.[18] Witness the kinds of action which the discovery of the BRCA 1 gene has precipitated. Bilateral mastectomy for teenage girls carrying the gene and having a 50% chance of developing breast cancer by the age of fifty seems somewhat irrational. However, where the presence of a specific mutation indicates the presence of a clinical abnormality and there is an effective treatment readily available, there is a therapeutic advantage in having access to the genetic testing. These factors determine the value of the information and should govern the practice of genetic counselling.

Genetic counselling: neutral or directed to human flourishing?

The issues confronting Jenny as she deals with the deaf couple who have sought her help raise questions about the very foundations of medical practice. What is disturbing for Jenny is that in this situation the definition of disease seems necessarily subjective. If this is true, there is little room for critique; respect for autonomy seems to require that the clinician accede to patient demand. Really what Jenny wants to know is whether there are some more objective bases for decision and how we might conceptualize these. It seems to me that part of the difficulty is an understanding of autonomy as freedom to act unhampered by external authority and its subsequent elevation to priority so that it becomes the single guiding principle for Jenny's practice.

In fact, it is possible for health-care professionals to respect the autonomy of patients if autonomy is seen as tempered by a concern for human flourishing which takes into account more than the desire to be self-directing. A fuller account of autonomy is needed to inform humane health care, and this fuller account can be derived from reflection on the nature of human well being.[19] Health care is a normative practice, and agnosticism with respect to norms transforms health care into commerce. If, however, deference to parental autonomy in this narrow sense directs the clinical geneticist, she must surely accede to all requests.

Conclusion

If Pope John Paul II is right to claim that 'The quality of a society and a civilization is measured by the respect shown to the weakest of its members,'[20] then perhaps we need to scrutinize the purpose of genetic counselling more critically. If the purpose is eugenic, in that we seek to eradicate those genes we regard as undesirable, then we face the charge of having used genetic information to discriminate between people. At least some of those who bear these disabilities regard such judgments as morally objectionable. They claim equal right to protection, before as well as after birth, a right guaranteed by the United Nations Declaration on the Rights of the Child (1959).

Finally, the question is whether we really want to bequeath to these chosen children a world in which we have suspended a universal commitment to the protection of human life in favour of the right to self-determination. Such a stance strikes at the very heart of the values taken as self-evident by the founders of modern democratic states. Before we embark on this course we ought to ask ourselves what has precipitated this change. We need to enquire whether our fragile virtue will not be irreparably harmed by embracing a rational solution to a dilemma which goes beyond the bounds of rationality and invites us to consider the mystery of our human life, here, together. As Robert Frost said, the construction of walls or dividing lines always seems to go against the mysterious urge of life itself. As I think about pre-natal genetic testing and counselling, his lines echo in my mind:

Before I built a wall,
I'd ask to know what
I was walling in or walling out,
And to whom I was like to give offence.[21]

And I wonder, if we are walling out imperfection in others, what are we to make of ourselves? Is it not better to accept some frailty and so stake a claim to a place in the human community?

Notes

1. I am grateful to the staff of the Queensland Clinical Genetics Service who discussed the paper with me, casting light on my own inaccuracies, errors and misunderstanding. I also presented an earlier version of this paper to the Annual Conference of the Catholic Moral Theologians Association of Australia and New Zealand and the advice of many there has been incorporated.

2. J. D. Howell, 'The History of Eugenics and the Future of Gene Therapy', *Journal of Clinical Ethics* 2 (40), 1991, 274–8.

3. J. M. Friedman, 'Eugenics and the "New Genetics"', *Perspectives in Biology and Medicine*, 35(1), 1991, 145–54.

4. S. G. Post, 'Selective Abortion and Gene Therapy: Reflections on Human Limits', *Human Gene Therapy* 2, 1991, 229–33. See also his *Inquiries in Bioethics*, Washington DC 1993, 7–21.

5. C. L. Bosk, *All God's Mistakes: Genetic Counselling in a Pediatric Hospital*, Chicago 1992, xv.

6. L. G. Biesecker, 'Orphan Tests', *Cambridge Quarterly of Health Care Ethics* 5, 1996, 300–6.

7. H. Jonas, The *Imperative of Responsibility*, Chicago 1984, 22.

8. K. O. Steel, 'The Road that I See. Implications of New Reproductive Technologies', *Cambridge Quarterly of Health Care Ethics* 4, 1995, 351–4.

9. Jonas, *Imperative of Responsibility* (n. 7), 39–40.

10. E. R. Hepburn, 'Genetic Testing and Early Diagnosis and Intervention: Boon or Burden?, *Journal of Medical Ethics* 22 (2), 1996, 105–10.

11. H. G. Gadamer, *The Enigma of Health*, Oxford 1996.

12. I will restrict my comments to genetic testing for predictive rather than strictly diagnostic purposes. I will also concentrate on pre-natal genetic counselling, for although I acknowledge that this may occupy only about a third of the total practice, it is the most contentious. I also presume that genetic counsellors apply strict standards of confidentiality, privacy and informed consent.

13. R. Chadwick, *Euroscreen Final Report. Genetic Screening: Ethical and Philosophical Perspectives*, 1997, 7.

14. A. Davis, 'Infanticide for the Handicapped Newborn – a secular rejection', *Journal of Medical Ethics* 13, 1988, 233.

15. Though spina bifida cannot be predicted by genetic tests.

16. D. Sanderson, 'Fear and Ignorance', *The Tablet*, 6 July 1996, 890.

17. Again issues of disclosure, confidentiality and privacy are crucial, and genetic counsellors seem to be cognizant of these and keen to promote a code of practice which protects clients and relatives.

18. I have dealt with these issues elsewhere, see my 'Genetic Testing', n. 10.

19. Here I am thinking of the powerful critique of the modern view of autonomy by Charles Taylor, *Sources of the Self*, Cambridge, Mass 1989, esp. 14, 495f.

20. Pope John II, Statement for the International Year of Disabled Persons, *Origins*, 7 May 1981, 747–50.

21. R. Frost, 'Mending Wall', *Selected Poems*, Harmondsworth 1955, 34.

The Moral Status of the Embryo

Maureen Junker-Kenny

How can one suggest reflection on the moral status of something that is smaller than a speck of dust? For some, the question of moral status would already be answered by this observation, and dismissed as impossible. But it is the different answers to this question which divide the legislation on biomedical matters in different countries. And if there are opposite legal positions, there must be a deeper philosophical controversy about the nature of this entity, its potential, relevant thresholds in its development, and the claims it may pose to society and the law as well as to the woman whose body is its host. What is under debate is whether the embryo can already be called human life, and, more to the point, whether it should be called a person and therefore enjoy the protection which this status accords: the human rights to life and bodily integrity.[1] The answer to this question will decide whether and if so, when, freezing, experimenting with and cloning of embryos should be permitted.

I would like to treat this discussion by first analysing two different arguments against ascribing any moral status of its own to the embryo or foetus:

(a) the British philosopher John Harris's thesis of a personhood which is empirically verifiable;

(b) the American feminist theologian Marjorie Maguire's theory of personhood through covenant. Do they give criteria for personhood? What significance do they attach to terms such as potential, relationality, and to different stages of development?

I shall contrast their theories with the opposing view, which interprets 'potential' as continuity and identity and thus ascribes personhood already to the zygote, i.e. the fertilized egg after the fusion of the nuclei of egg and sperm and before cell division. Here, I shall begin with the insight into the hermeneutical and practical character inherent in all definitions of human life and personhood. I shall then examine from this perspective the objections made against claiming personhood for this stage: the limits of the embryo's potential as shown in the need for implantation into a supporting ecosystem, the mother's womb, the fact that part of what develops from the zygote will be the placenta and not the foetus and the possibility of twinning as an argument against individuation. In my third part, I shall outline the practical consequences of my position as developed in Part Two for concrete issues of legislation, namely embryo freezing, experimentation and cloning.

I. The embryo – not a person in its own right

(a) Personhood as an empirically verifiable feature

One position in the present philosophical debate on personhood is that a person can only be someone to whom the empirical traits of persons apply. Only those humans count as persons who are actually and instantly able to give evidence of their capacity for reason and self-consciousness.[2]

In this view, to be a person in the *moral* sense and to be human in the *biological* sense are two independent factors which intersect only partially. 'Not all persons are human, and not all humans are persons.'[3] But is this a correct premise? If this is true, then human embryos, newborn babies and the mentally handicapped or patients in an irreversible coma are humans but not persons. Intelligent animals such as whales, dolphins and chimpanzees have a greater claim to the title of person than these humans.[4] This is indeed the consequence which the Australian philosopher Peter Singer draws. Another representative of this view is the British philosopher John Harris. In his article 'Embryos and hedgehogs: On the moral status of the embryo', he states: 'There are really only two ways in which this question can be approached: one is in terms of the actual moral status of the embryo at any one time, and the other is in terms of the potential of the embryo to acquire a moral status or personhood which it does not at present possess.'[5] Harris goes for the first approach and dismisses the second: 'I argue that the moral status of the embryo and indeed of any individual is determined by its possession of those features which make normal adult human individuals morally more important than sheep or goats or embryos'(79). He declines to name these criteria, but it would be safe to assume that rationality and some kind of self-reflection would belong to them. Without these morally relevant features, however, any being would have no more value than those 'unique, fully formed, sentient' creatures which, as he says, might constitute 'our Sunday roast' (69–70). This may be a needlessly offensive way to put it, but it is certainly clear. Harris might still be able to speak of persons as bearers of unalienable rights, although it is doubtful if there is a basis in Utilitarianism for thinking the term 'unalienable', since there is no concept of the human person as a limit to the desires of the majority, i.e. as someone who should not be instrumentalized. But however these rights are to be described, they do not belong to members of the human species by definition, but only to those actually able to demonstrate their use of reason. And clearly, embryos do not count among them.

(b) Personhood through covenant

A different argument for the same position that embryos have no inherent rights of their own is put forward by the American feminist theologian Marjorie Reiley Maguire. Her theory of covenant is not based on any empirical definition which identifies, as Engelhardt and Harris do, the actual 'performance' of a being with the 'competence' the being has in principle (to use a distinction of Chomsky's). She adopts a 'relational' approach.[6] Her search for 'the precise formal element that constitutes personhood' (103) leads her to the following thesis: 'I would propose that the only person who can be the initiator of covenantal love for prenatal life, bringing that life into the reality of human community and thereby making it a person, is the woman in whose womb the pregnancy' (not the embryo!) 'exists. The personhood begins when the bearer of life, the mother, makes a covenant of life with the developing life within her to bring it to birth . . . The moment which begins personhood, then, is the moment when the mother accepts the pregnancy. At the moment when the mother bonds with the foetus, the foetus becomes a Thou to her rather than an It . . . It is the mother who makes the foetus a person. After that point life is sacred because it is sacred to her' (109–10). If the mother does not consent to the pregnancy, no personhood is established. She concludes: 'The discarding of some of those fertilized ova, and even experimentation on them, is not necessarily immoral if there are no persons floating in petri dishes' (117).

This position is a step beyond the actualistic one, where present command of reason is the defining factor for personhood – as long as it lasts. For Maguire, there is a recognition element to personhood. Her argumentation shows that we can welcome someone who is less than rational into our lives and accord it the status of a 'Thou', instead of the 'It' of the Sunday roast.

However, her theory is based on two explicit presuppositions which are far from evident:

1. 'I believe that no one has a right to life, deserving of full protection of the law, when that life is totally dependent on the body of another human

being for its life support' (102). This is a far-reaching claim. Not only when the life of the mother is threatened does a conflict arise between the rights to life of both the embryo and the mother; now the fact of dependence alone is enough to put the embryo's right to life into question. What I find missing here is the recognition that except in cases of rape, pregnancies are the results of the actions of people, and we are responsible for the consequences of our actions. Although degrees of responsibility vary with regard to circumstances, it is not convincing to say that the embryo imposes itself on the life of the mother. If it wasn't for the prior actions of others, the embryo would not be able to make such a claim.

2. The second presupposition already showed up in the line, 'the only person who can be the initiator of covenantal love for prenatal life, *bringing that life into the reality of human community and thereby making it a person*, is the woman'. She states explicitly: 'Sociality is the touchstone of personhood . . . that is why the biological side of personhood is not sufficient of itself to constitute the formal element of the beginning of personhood' (114). So sociality makes a person? This view plays down the other pole that is decisive: the element of spontaneity, reflexivity, prior familiarity with myself which cannot be explained from intersubjectivity. If this element is not recognized, we would not be able to distinguish between autonomy and heteronomy, authentic selfhood and unquestioning obedience to the rules of convention. The embryo does not possess any actual reflexivity, it only possesses it potentially. But it should be clear that no one becomes a person by virtue of the human community alone.

In summary, the language of covenant barely disguises the feudal relationship proposed here: it is a one-sided power to elect, exercised among humans.

Even with regard to God, the history of theology has witnessed fierce debates on whether election can be squared with the universality of God's love towards humanity. Maguire's interpretation turns pregnancy into a one-sided power-relationship which is asserted and celebrated in a way that denies the 'mutuality' otherwise prominent in feminist ethics. Here this power relationship is asserted and celebrated. Against the absolute power of the electing mother, the embryo has no claim. This is rather like the late mediaeval concept of God's absolute power that led philosophers like Hans Blumenberg to claim that the human subject had to insist on his freedom in order to escape from the arbitrariness of God's unpredictable will.[7]

II. The zygote as person

Before we go on to consider more definitions of potential and personhood from the opposite side, it is time to reflect on the status and implications of this exercise itself.

(a) The hermeneutical circle inherent in definitions of human personhood

It should have become clear by now that definitions of personhood are not lofty philosophical speculations but have an immediate practical significance. The question of personhood is a philosophical one in which we state our self-understanding as humans. Whom do we accept as a member of our species who is entitled to protection and care?

Any definition of the beginning (and end) of human personhood is caught in a hermeneutical circle. We define its starting point because we want to act in a certain way, and we act according to how we have defined it.[8] If we consider the moment of implantation in the uterus, or the presence of brain activity, or the ability to communicate, as the starting-point for ascribing personhood, we are free to use the embryo prior to this stage in any way we consider useful.

Each definition has a practical intent. Once we ascribe human life and personhood to an entity, we want to protect it. If one wants to give maximum protection, one has to use a minimal definition, such as the new genetic unity created by egg and sperm. A maximal definition of human life, such as the ability to communicate, or to act independently, offers minimal protection to the stages prior to these competencies and after they have been lost. A minimal definition of the beginning of human personal life that offers maximal protection would be: once there is an auto-reproductive unit in which the nuclei of the sperm and the egg have fused, this new entity should count as having human dignity and human rights to life and the inviolability of its (his or her) body. This unit should be referred to as the 'embryo', not as 'pre-embryo', as it is sometimes done. It should be clear that this usage is already based on the decision that no moral status can be ascribed to the product of conception in the first fourteen days of its existence, and this decision is clothed in the language of science. To call the zygote 'pre-embryo' makes one of many stages in its development, namely implantation, definitive for attributing basic rights to it.[9] In contrast, it makes sense to follow the ethical principle stated by Dietmar Mieth: human life has to be respected and fostered as a fundamental and integral value. 'Integral' means that no lines can be drawn between a stage of no value, where it is at our disposal, and a different stage when it acquires full value.[10]

It is therefore a *practical* decision at what developmental stage we attribute human personhood to the embryo, foetus, or newborn, and it is in the interest of the earliest possible protection of 'the weakest link in the chain of the human species'[11] if one states that this new genetic unity is a person. Let us hear the case of those for whom the unique genetic individuality of the zygote merits its designation as the beginning of 'human personhood' because of the identity and continuity of its development.

(b) 'Potential' as identity and continuity

Schockenhoff insists that the only relevant line that can be drawn is the 'radically new beginning' which happens when the fertilized egg becomes a zygote (307). To those who argue for taking the beginnings of brain formation as the decisive threshold for personhood, he answers: this would be drawing an artificial line into a continuous process of development. 'The possibility for the later emergence of mind, consciousness and freedom is there in principle from conception onwards; it becomes more probable after implantation and the development of the primitive streak; but the question is whether this probability factor justifies drawing a demarcation to which such a high anthropological relevance and the corresponding normative consequences are attached' (cf. 309–10 n. 41). In Schockenhoff's view, there is one process of development; in principle, all the emergent features are founded on the basic autoreproductive unit of the zygote, and it would be arbitrary to say any particular stage introduces such a qualitative difference that only from then onwards there would be a sufficient basis for personhood. It is one human being that has all the dispositions for later realizations within itself: it is a potential marked by identity on a genetic basis, and by continuity both temporally and substantially. Therefore formulations such as Harris's, that the embryo is 'potentially a human being; it will eventually become a human being' (312 n. 46) are misleading. Human embryos do not develop *into* humans, but *as* humans. And here, 'the point of the potentiality argument is that what is crucial for being granted a right to life is the capability to become a moral subject, not the feature realized at any actual moment. This potential to become a moral subject does not begin at birth or with coming of age, it unfolds on the basis of the whole natural process of development and is part of a continuous context of human life from the earliest embryonic stage onwards. We are asked to respect the future chances for life of an individual at every point of her development in time, even if she does not yet have a reflective concept of the continuity of herself' (313f.).

However, to attribute human personhood to the zygote does not imply that in ethical dilemmas it is always the embryo who 'wins'. It allows one to set up the dilemma and ask whether the right of the embryo to survive is equal, superior or subordinated to the mother's rights to life and self-determination.

III. Objections

(a) The natural limits of the embryo's potential

But what if the 'capability to become a moral subject' presupposes more than the embryo has within itself, namely implantation into the mother's womb? Dame Helen Warnock points to this lack of capacity: 'To say that eggs and sperm cannot by themselves become human, but only if bound together, does not seem to me to differentiate them from the early embryo which by itself will not become human either, but will die unless it is implanted.'[12] True, the only thing an embryo will do by itself is to divide and differentiate its unique genetic combination. If it does not implant *in vivo* or if it is withheld from implantation *in vitro*, it will not develop further.

The counter-argument to this point which identifies 'potential' or 'capacity' with the ability to create one's own conditions for survival, is to highlight that all life needs a supporting eco-system and is inter-dependent: 'Fish need water, humans need air, embryos need wombs' (Janet Soskice). This analogy does not imply that women only count as context for embryos, nor indeed that all embryos need are wombs; it illustrates that the fact that we need supporting conditions to survive and develop does not speak against our personhood.

(b) Is the placenta a person?

Here, the argument is not that there is too little to qualify for personhood, but too much: at this stage, even before the new auto-reproductive unit starts reproducing itself through cell division, it is too early to differentiate between what will become the foetus and what will be the placenta.

The trouble with this (and the following) objection is its biological essentialism. To give personhood status to the zygote before the differentiation into the body of the embryo and the placenta occurs does not personalize the placenta. It extends the protection zone of human dignity to the earliest stage where the nuclei of the gametes have fused. The fact that the cells developing from this unit are totipotent cannot reduce the dignity of the new genetic unit.

(c) Twinning

It can't be *a* person because it might be *two* persons. Individuation must have occurred for it to be a personal human life, and that only happens by day fourteen (implantation). So this is the earliest time that we could speak of personhood.

Again, my point is that if one is aware of the hermeneutical and practical character of one's definition of personhood, one cannot confound the biological and metaphysical levels in such a way as to say that the possibility of twinning speaks against the personhood of the embryo. If one's practical intention is to protect the earliest possible stage of human life against instrumentalization, it does not lessen but rather doubles the dignity of the zygote if it is not one future child, but two who enjoy this protection. We already approach these data from an ethical viewpoint which goes into our definition of what we have before us 'empirically': human tissue, or a bearer of human rights.

Another reason is given by Schockenhoff: a philosophical interpretation of embryonic development cannot only focus on the rare event of twinning (or, for that matter, of moles, or of parthenogenesis); it also has to give an adequate explanation for the fact that most zygotes do not divide into two individuals and its totipotent cells differentiate into the various organic areas of *one* human being (cf. 308).

III. Consequences for concrete issues for legislation

In the abortion debates of the 1970s, things looked much more simple. If one was pro-baby, one was pro-life. Since the arrival of techniques of assisted procreation, this equation is not valid any more. It is now possible to be pro-baby and anti-life. If one is convinced of the right to have a child by all means, one will accept conditions which others would judge to be at odds with the dignity of the embryo and child: embryo wastage, anonymous donors, eugenic or sex selection. As it should have become clear by now, it is not only the good of the infertile couples which is at stake in infertility treatments, but also the rights of the future child which sometimes conflict with the parents' desperate wish for offspring of their own. Therefore, a balance needs to be struck between the interests of the couples and of the embryo whenever they are competing. Immediate issues here are the freezing, experimentation and cloning of embryos.

1. Embryo freezing
The medical advantages to embryo freezing are:
– the woman has to undergo ovarian stimulation and egg harvesting only once,

– the chances of the second and third cycles being successful are slightly higher,
– only one or two embryos would need to be replaced, thus reducing the complications of multiple pregnancies.

The ethical problem, however, is that, depending on one's answer to the question of the beginning of human personhood, freezing of embryos at the four-cell stage could mean to have 'human beings in waiting', and most of them waiting to be discarded after a fixed period, or to be kept indefinitely, even after the lifetime of their parents. This last way out, however, is not an option, if one insists, as the body of Protestant, Anglican and Orthodox Churches in Europe does in a position paper of the European Ecumenical Commission for Church and Society, that the biological and relational aspects should not be separated and that the 'parental or marital context' needs to be ensured.[13]

A balance between the interests of the couples and the dignity of the embryo would be achieved with 'pro-nuclear' freezing. The fertilized egg is frozen before syngamy, i.e. before the genetic material from both gametes combines to form the new and unique genetic individuality which is auto-reproductive and able to divide. This freezing of the pre-zygote is practised e.g. in Germany to fulfill the demands of the German Embryo Protection Act. Freezing at the pro-nuclear stage, however, has the scientific disadvantage of not being able to single out the 'healthy-looking' embryos, and thus slightly reduces the success rate.

2. Experimentation

The position paper of the European Ecumenical Commission for Church and Society submitted to the Council of Europe summarizes the different positions of the member churches on the status of the embryo – from regarding it as human tissue to seeing it as a person – and states its disapproval of creating spare embryos for research: 'Christian anthropology does not allow a separation of biological or relational aspects . . . Speaking about a human embryo as a child should take place . . . in the "parental or marital context". . . So-called "spare embryos" . . . are artificially placed outside the parental context. As such, they are still human embryos, but at least in practice, no future children or persons to be' (57). With regard to research on them, e.g. to help people with Parkinson's disease, they conclude: 'We want to make it clear that what has been developed to help childless couples should not be used as a key to open up other research areas.' As a general rule, they endorse 'in dubiis, abstine' ('if in doubt, refrain'). For some of them this means that 'non-therapeutic embryo research should be prohibitied' (58). For others it means that it should only be allowed in a 'case-by-case approach where the researcher has to give sufficient reasons' (cf. 58). If research is going to be permitted, they call for a 'broadly based (!) licensing body to monitor and control the research'.

3. Cloning

What the European Ecumenical Commission for Church and Society demands, that a technology developed to help childless couples for the medical aims of other people should not be used, has a direct bearing on the specific use of cloning, which has now been permitted through a significant change of language, the 'distinction of the year' 1997, according to D. Mieth: 'reproductive versus non-reproductive cloning'. What is prohibited is reproductive cloning, but this term 'reproductive' no longer denotes sperm, egg and all embryos – as in an earlier Declaration of the Council of Ministers in the European Union – but now means only those embryos which are going to be implanted. This restriction of the meaning of 'reproductive', which in effect declares the cloning of embryos for research legal, is an example of language policy that veils the real intentions. It promotes also what the Protestant Churches in Europe do not want to be allowed, namely using the IVF technique outside the context which justifies its origin, namely of helping infertile couples to have children. Cloning embryos to be used for tissue development for organ donation is not within these boundaries.

It is both exciting and awesome to be at this threshold where new possibilities for curing diseases are beckoning, but where the human person is also being redefined. I hope to have shown why the way in which we define and treat the embryo – as human tissue and raw material for our rational purposes, or at laast as human life with a moral claim – says something about how we see ourselves and who we want to be in the future.

Notes

1. The decisive question is, when does human *personhood* begin? Human *life* clearly begins at fertilization, so it is misleading to say that 'the embryo *becomes* human'. Genetically, the zygote *is* distinctively human already. But on what level is the decision on human personhood made, and on which criteria is it based?

2. Cf. the discussion in Schockenhoff, *Ethik des Lebens*, Mainz 1993, 45–9, 87–103.

3. Tristram Engelhardt, *The Foundations of Bioethics*, New York and Oxford 1986, 107. See also id., 'Entscheidungsprobleme konkurrierender Interessen von Mutter and Fötus', in V. Braun et al. (ed.), *Ethische und rechtliche Fragen der Gentechnologie und der Reproduktionsmedizin*, Munich 1987, 150–9.

4. Cf. Schockenhoff, *Ethik des Lebens* (n. 2), 45–9.

5. In A. Dyson and J. Harris (eds), *Experiments on Embryos*, London 1990, 65–81. Further page references in the text.

6. 'The biological approach (to personhood) never clearly shows why the newly conceived or developing prenatal life should be considered the moral and legal peer of a newborn baby rather than ontologically closer to a separate sperm and egg' ('Personhood, Covenant, and Abortion', in P. Jung and T. Shannon [eds], *Abortion and Catholicism*, New York 1988, 100–20: 106). Further page references in the text. She refers to Charles Curran's distinction between 'individual-biological', 'relational', 'multiple' and 'conferred rights' criteria ('Abortion: Ethical Aspects', in *Transition and Tradition in Moral Theology*, Notre Dame 1979, 207–29). Other members of the 'relational' school are the French moral theologians he mentions (228 n. 10) (cf. *Lumière et vie* 21, no. 109, 1972).

7. Hans Blumenberg, *The Legitimacy of the Modern Age* (second revised ed. Cambridge, Mass. 1983).

8. Here I am following the argumentation of Dietmar Mieth, *Geburtenregelung. Ein Konflikt in der katholischen Kirche*, Mainz 1990, 78–82, 95–6. A similar evaluation can be found in Paul Ricoeur's discussion of 'respect for persons at the "beginning of life"'. In Kant's 'bipolar opposition of persons and things, the distinction between mode of beings remained inseparable from practice, that is, from the manner of treating persons and things . . . To be sure, the identification of thresholds and degrees marking the appearance of properties of being is dependent on science alone. But the ontological tenor assigned to the predicate "potential" in the expression "potential human person" is perhaps not separable from the manner of "treating" beings corresponding to these various stages. Manner of being and manner of treating would seem to be mutually determined in the formation of prudential judgments occasioned by each advance in the power that technology confers today on humankind over life in its beginnings' (*Oneself as Another*, Chicago 1992, 270–2).

9. This insight into the inevitable hermeneutical circle between the practical interest of the person defining and the resulting definition is missing in T. Shannon's and A. Wolters' critique of the philosophical essentialism of Vatican statements on this question. Their 'Reflections on the Moral Status of the Pre-Embryo', in T. Shannon (ed.), *Bioethics*, Mahwah, NJ [4]1994, 36–60, however, seem to replace one essentialism with a different, biological one. The middle route is to take biological observations of stages and thresholds seriously enough to avoid the charge of nominalism, yet see the practical character of any definition of the beginning of human personhood. Ricoeur speaks of the 'complex play between science and wisdom' (272) and rightly analyses any definition as a prudential judgment which has to be all the more cautious in the context of scientific manipulation of embryos (*Oneself*, 272–3).

10. Cf. Mieth, *Geburtenregelung* (n. 8), 95–6.

11. Cf. Dominique Folscheid, 'The Status of the Embryo from a Christian Perspective', in *Studies in Christian Ethics* 9, 1996, 1–21: 21.

12. Quoted in John Harris, 'Embryos and Hedgehogs', 72.

13. EECCS Bioethics Working Group, *Drawing the Line – The Ethics of Biotechnology*, Occasional Paper No. 5, Brussels, 1997, 57.

III · Social Policies

Genetics and the Future of American Law and Policy

M. Cathleen Kaveny

Introduction

The groundbreaking possibilities of contemporary genetic research catapulted to the forefront of American public consciousness in February 1997, when the Scottish scientists Ian Wilmut and Keith Campbell announced that on the 277th attempt, they had successfully cloned a lamb from a cell taken from the mammary gland of an adult ewe. A picture of the cloned lamb, whom the scientists named 'Dolly' after the country singer Dolly Parton, graced the pages of almost every newspaper and news magazine in the country. The lamb's placid, unthreatening visage furnished an ironic contrast to the fearful spectre of mass-produced, genetically designed *human* clones conjured by many commentators discussing this scientific milestone.

Law and policy makers were not oblivious to the deep public consternation precipitated by Dolly's appearance. Almost immediately, President Bill Clinton issued an executive order prohibiting any use of federal funds for research on human cloning and gave the National Bioethics Advisory Commission ninety days to investigate the question. The Commission's report, issued in June 1997, called for a three-to-five year federal ban on all attempts to 'create a child using somatic cell nuclear transfer cloning'.[1] It did not, however, go so far as to recommend prohibiting the cloning of human embryos for research purposes, provided that they are not implanted into a woman's uterus and brought to term. Similar activities took place on the state level; bills that would ban all attempts to clone a human being were introduced in a number of state legislatures.

To a casual observer, American law and policy makers might appear to have mustered a swift and appropriate response to this sudden collision of real life and science fiction. Yet a closer examination of the development of the American stance toward cloning reveals serious inadequacies. Most generally, it proceeds as if the salient moral and policy issues can appropriately be considered in abstraction from other questions raised by the burgeoning panoply of genetic research, spearheaded by the Human Genome Project.[2] Such abstraction carries with it three dangers.

First, the policy issues raised by cloning will likely be treated too narrowly, because the terms of the debate have been cast in a way that sidesteps closely related and far more controversial matters. For example, the National Bioethics Commission deliberately ignored questions regarding the moral permissibility of experimenting on human embryos, which would be necessary not only to pursue cloning but also many other types of genetic research. Second, by focussing attention upon the publicly fascinating but practically remote scenario of human cloning, policymakers may distract attention from more pressing particular questions posed by other advances in genetic research, such as how to deal with the vast amounts of genetic information about individuals and their families that is quickly becoming available. Third, and more generally, the pressure to address a high-profile problem such as cloning in a rapid, reactive and piecemeal fashion unhelpfully distracts policymakers from the more painstaking task of fundamentally re-evaluating the legal, ethical and regulatory framework that will guide our practices in the area of genetics.

How, then, should legal and social policy go about addressing the questions raised by contemporary genetics? In order to counteract the deficiencies illustrated by the American response to cloning, our social policy must coherently address three fundamental, interrelated questions. What constraints should be placed on the means used to obtain genetic knowledge or make progress in treating genetic diseases? Second, what limitations should we observe on the use of genetic knowledge, whether it pertains to humanity in general, or to specific human persons? Third, assuming that a society's laws furnish some elements of the interpretative framework in which its members view themselves and one another, how do we want the law to shape our minds and hearts as we explore the implications of our new knowledge of human genetics?[3] In the remainder of this article, I will suggest that the tools of contemporary American law and policy are far from adequate to the task.

I. Limitations on the means used to obtain genetic knowledge

Incredibly, much of the genetic research carried out in the United States is unconstrained by legal or regulatory strictures regarding the means used to conduct that research. In large part, this phenomenon is attributable to the distribution of law-making responsibility between the federal government and the states on the one hand, and between state legislatures and state courts on the other.

First, genetic research lies at the intersection of medical-ethical law and family law, both of which have traditionally been the province of the states, rather than the federal government. Accordingly, the United States Congress has thus far chosen to make policy in the general area of research involving human subjects indirectly rather than directly, by placing conditions on the receipt of financial assistance from the federal government. For over twenty years now, elaborate federal regulations designed to protect human subjects in research have been in place; however, these regulations apply *only* to research underwritten in some way by federal monies.[4] Research conducted in private facilities and with privately donated funds is not subject to those regulations, and is largely unmonitored. R. Alto Charo, an ethicist who sits on the National Bioethics Advisory Commission, has remarked, 'We have better information about animal experiments than we do about human experiments.'[5]

Second, at the state level, novel issues of family law and medical-ethical law have usually not been addressed by legislatures enacting a pro-active, coherent, generally applicable policy, but by the courts, who are forced to deal with them in a reactive, *ad hoc* manner. State legislatures, of course, are free to enact laws dealing with cutting-edge issues at the borders of medicine and reproduction. However, many states have demurred not only from banning, but even from regulating innovative techniques such as surrogate motherhood, sperm or oocyte donation, *in vitro* fertilization and implantation of fertilized embryos.[6]

The most controversial policy question regarding the means used by contemporary genetics involves the permissibility of various experimental interventions on the early human embryo. A brief survey of current law on the subject confirms how far the United States is from implementing a reflective, rationally defensible policy on the salient issues. At present, federal law imposes guidelines upon federally funded experiments involving human foetuses, and bans the use of federal funding for research involving the creation of human embryos *in vitro* solely for research purposes.[7] However, no federal regulations bar or restrict the use of human embryos or foetuses in privately funded research.[8]

Generally speaking, state law provides little additional guidance. Some states (e.g., Massachusetts and Louisiana) have enacted stringent statutes pertaining to experimentation on both the foetus and the embryo. A few others restrict research on foetuses, including those destined for abortion.

However, these bans arguably do not apply to unimplanted embryos. Most states have passed no legislation at all dealing with pre-natal experimentation.

Furthermore, the lack of comprehensive, pro-active legislative guidance from the states in the area of reproductive technologies is likely to spill over into closely related areas of genetics. For example, a fertility clinic in Virginia offers interested clients the option of testing the embryos produced by *in vitro* fertilization for genetic defects before deciding whether to implant them in the woman's uterus.[9] There is no reason to think that such clinics will refrain from offering other genetic services as soon as the technology becomes available, whether or not it has been subjected to careful testing. Eventually, such services could include pre-implantation somatic gene therapy, both to remedy a defect or to confer some type of genetic enhancement (such as height or intelligence).[10] More distantly, they could also include untested ventures into germ line therapy. The comparatively remote possibility of a lawsuit brought by an unsatisfied customer is not likely to deter the more enterprising clinics, particularly given that developing foetuses can be aborted at the first sign of abnormality.

II. Limits on the use of genetic knowledge

There are approximately 5,700 known genetic disorders, of which over 300 are detectable with genetic testings, including cystic fibrosis, sickle cell anaemia, and Huntington's Disease.[11] We have recently identified genes that indicate a greater susceptibility to breast cancer, colon cancer, and heart disease. The success of the Human Genome Project augurs the speedy discovery of many other genes contributing to various types of human illness.

Once a defective gene is isolated, it is a relatively short scientific step to the development of a test that will allow us to identify its presence in an adult, a child, an unborn foetus, or even an embryo *in vitro*. Unfortunately, developing safe and effective therapies for the diseases we learn to detect is a far more difficult and time-consuming task. Thus, for the foreseeable future, the most pressing policy issues generated by contemporary genetic advances will revolve around the dissemination and use of more or less unalterable genetic information.[12] Current legal and bioethical discussions cluster on two closely related sets of issues. First, who should be able to obtain information about an individual's genetic profile? Second, what is the range of permissible decisions made on the basis of such information?[13]

Much of the current writing on genetics, medicine and society attempts to address the intertwined problems of the dissemination and use of genetic information without calling into question the dominant framework of contemporary bioethical policy, particularly its emphasis on the autonomy and privacy of the individual seeking genetic testing.

For example, in accordance with that dominant framework, many bioethicists strongly champion the right of each competent individual to seek and obtain information about her own genetic make-up. Echoing the contemporary emphasis upon expansive choice in reproductive matters, most also advocate broad parental access to pre-natal genetic diagnosis, as well as legally unimpeded parental decision-making on the basis of such information. Most writers are quick to point out that their approach would prohibit government-mandated abortion and selected implantation as well as governmental restrictions on such procedures.[14]

At the same time, emphasis on preserving a patient's 'genetic privacy' against the outside world is growing. Analogizing genetic information to other highly sensitive information such as a person's HIV status, a growing body of bioethical literature would prohibit physicians from disclosing it to anyone without the patient's express consent. Particular emphasis focusses on safeguarding genetic information from employers and health insurers, who normally have significant access to an individual's medical records.[15] At the same time, there have been somewhat clumsy efforts to render genetic informaton 'irrelevant' to the decision-making of employers and health insurers by *fiat* of federal legislation. For example, the Health Insurance Portability and Accountability Act of 1996[16] prohibits group health plans from denying individuals coverage on the basis of genetic information, or using such information to justify charging such persons higher premiums. (However, it does not prevent plans from adjusting the rates they charge *to employers* on that basis.) On the employment front, the Americans with Disabilities Act of 1990[17] has been interpreted to prohibit employers from taking into account genetic information about currently asymptomatic applicants in making job offers. (They can, however, obtain access to such information after offering employment to an applicant.)[18]

At least superficially, then, American biomedical policy appears to be dealing with the challenges presented by contemporary genetics in an adequate manner. However, I believe that appearance to be deeply deceptive. The genetic 'revolution' is aptly named. Rather than fitting safely within established categories, our new-found knowledge of the human genome will force us to rethink four fundamental assumptions that have come to dominate bioethics and biolaw over the past thirty years. These assumptions concern the nature of the human person; illness and death; the physician-care giver relationship; and the meaning of medical information and the purpose of informed consent. As discussed below, I believe that any attempt to solve the ethical and legal questions created by genetics without making appropriate alterations to the regnant assumptions in these four areas will be destined to failure.

Personhood

First, contemporary genetics calls into question the reigning understanding of personhood. Despite recent challenges to this view posed by theoretical philosophy, applied bioethics generally continues to assume that competent patients should be treated as autonomous decision-makers whose core identities and interests are sharply distinct not only from that of their family members, but even from their own bodies. On this view, an individual person *has* a body, and *chooses* to initiate or maintain familial relationships.

In contrast, contemporary genetics erodes the contemporary tendency to view human persons as essentially minds or wills who inhabit their bodies. Our mental qualities and personality traits are likely to be as strongly rooted in our genetic heritage as are our bodily characteristics. Mind, heart and soul, we are embodied beings. Furthermore, genetics suggests that at our very core, we are not isolated, atomistic individuals, but more like members of a 'clan'. Our genetic heritage binds us vertically to our biological parents and biological children in complicated webs of inheritance and transmission encompassing physical, mental and emotional traits. It links us horizontally to our brothers and sisters, whose genetic inheritance tells us something about the characteristics that might – or might not – also be our own.

Once bioethics acknowledges the degree to which contemporary genetics challenges its fundamental assumptions about the human person, it will be forced to grapple with the deeply discordant way that contemporary social policy increasingly portrays familial relationships as essentially matters of voluntary and affective choice. Over the past two decades, the use of anonymous sperm and egg donors to facilitate parenthood for those who are unable or unwilling to procreate in the customary manner has become increasingly common. Genetic testing may pull such donors out of the darkness of anonymity into a peculiar twilight of distance and intimacy. A child may learn that she has inherited the sperm donor's eye colour, height, tendency toward diabetes, analytic ability and nervous temperament. By discovering her own genetic make-up, that child can come in some sense to know the man who is her biological father. Yet, in the end, he will remain fundamentally a stranger, since neither she nor her mother will ever have even one opportunity to form the integrated acquaintance with him that comes only through some type of personal encounter. This unstable combination of knowledge and ignorance, of presence and absence, is likely to be satisfactory to no one – not to the child, nor to the child's mother, who probably chose to conceive by an anonymous sperm donation in order to guarantee the biological father's absence from her family structure.

Illness and Death

Second, contemporary bioethics tends to construe illness and death as external forces that attack human beings from without. The individual patient's body is frequently, if tacitly, understood as the battlefield between her 'self' and the invading sources of illness. Viruses and bacterial infections are depicted as invading marauders; even cancer has been understood as triggered by carcinogens contaminating the body and turning it against itself. The discovery that many diseases have a strong genetic component poses a radical challenge to this understanding of illness and death. Rather than constituting the neutral ground where the forces of life combat the forces of disintegration, the human body now appears to conspire in its own decay. The seeds of death are sown at the same time as the seeds of life: the initial combination of maternal and paternal genetic material at the time of fertilization. They are ineluctable.

If American law and policy makers take seriously the 'internal' model of disease and death offered to us by genetics, we will no longer be able to content ourselves with misguided and piecemeal efforts to mend our health insurance system. True insurance contracts are designed to manage the risk of financial loss caused by catastrophic events whose occurrence is unpredictable in particular instances, although the frequency of their occurrence within a large group of insured is susceptible to fairly accurate estimation. The pure example of insurance is indemnification against the loss caused by natural disasters. But unlike fires or floods, illness and death now do not present themselves as purely random occurrences that might – or might not – strike any one of us at any given time. It increasingly appears that each human being is genetically 'programmed' for susceptibility to certain types of illness.

Widespread genetic testing wil enable individuals to discover at least something of their genetic frailties and the illnesses to which they are susceptible. But the possession of such knowledge renders health insurance a practical impossibility, at least with respect to genetically predictable illnesses. Some policy makers have suggested that we simply deny insurers access to genetic information. Yet the very fact that policy holders have it will skew the system; rational purchasers will seek coverage only at times when they are likely to need it, and put their money to better use at times when they are likely to be healthy. An insurance system cannot allow such practices, any more than it can allow home-owners to purchase flood insurance when the river is rising, or fire insurance when the engines are rolling.

Consequently, as genetic knowledge progresses, the question facing American society will not be whether everyone should have access to health insurance, which indemnifies persons for the catastrophic costs associated with the unknown risks of illness. It rather will be whether everyone should have access to health care as a social entitlement, no matter what we come to learn about their likelihood of developing medical problems.[19] Unfortunately, the utter failure of our most recent efforts at health reform do not give cause for optimism about the answer.

The Medical Relationship

The third feature of contemporary biomedical policy under siege by contemporary genetics is its conception of the nature and purpose of the medical relationship. That relationship has typically been construed as a dyadic partnership between the patient and the physician, who serves as the patient's chief strategist in the battle against illness. Privacy is a crucial element of this relationship; the physician is expected assiduously to gather information about matters affecting the patient's health, and just as assiduously to safeguard it against disclosure. The operative presumption is that medical information about an individual justifiably concerns only that individual. Except in narrowly defined situations, the physician's fiduciary obligation with respect to private information runs solely to her patient.[20]

However, recent developments in genetics call into question the dyadic character of the physician-patient relationship, and undermine the very concept of 'private' information. When an individual seeks information about her own genetic profile, her physician learns not only about her, but also something about the likely genetic make-up of her parents, her siblings, and her children. Unless a patient maintains sharp boundaries of secrecy at home, her family members will be told something about themselves. What duties of confidentiality does a physician have to these 'shadow patients'? Suppose, for example, that a physician discovers that the man whom a patient has always considered to be her biological father could not possibly be so? Does a child have a right to know her genetic heritage when it conclusively reveals that her mother committed adultery?[21] Conversely, does a physician have any obligation to seek out shadow patients in order to disclose possibly life-saving genetic information? Suppose that a physician learns that a patient's estranged sibling has a strong possibility of suffering from the same genetic defect?

Addressing these questions adequately may require both patients and physicians to rethink their obligations in a more 'clan-based' way. Perhaps we need to encourage patients who want to obtain their genetic profile to view their responsibilities as analogous to those of a *pater* or *mater familias*. They need to consider what effect that information will have on, and what decisions it will require from, other members of the family whom it concerns. Correlatively, physicians may need to resurrect and update the concept of the 'family doctor' in order to make sense of their obligations with respect to genetic information that is essentially information about a family unit, although its source is one particular member.

Medical information and informed consent

Fourth and finally, the very nature of medical information and informed consent is likely to change as a result of contemporary genetics. Most importantly, genetics will alter the purpose of conveying medical information to patients. As bioethics and biolaw developed, the information sought by and provided to a patient was generally designed to enable her to make a specific decision: whether to accept or refuse a particular medical intervention recommended by her physician. This understanding of the purpose of medical information reflects the roots of the doctrine of informed consent in the tort law of battery, which basically prohibits one person from touching another without her consent.

In contrast, the provision of genetic information to an individual is not designed to facilitate a decision about a separate medical intervention; in most cases, the very provision of such information *is* the intervention. Genetic information is far broader in focus than the information conveyed in a medical context; it confers a type of self-knowledge that will form the basis for a wide variety of choices over the course of a whole life. At least until gene therapy is far more advanced, the response to acquiring genetic information about oneself will be acceptance, not decision.

Moreover, contemporary genetics will require us to think about the meaning of medical information in a radically different fashion. While information provided to patients in the context of traditional medical decision-making frequently requires them to grapple with probabilities, these probabilities are quite narrowly focussed on the possible outcomes of a well-defined choice (e.g., for or against surgery). In contrast, genetic information requires persons to think in a probabilistic manner that can be far more complicated and open-ended than information designed to facilitate particular health care decisions.

More specifically, the presence of a defective gene means different things in different situations. In the case of genetically dominant disorders, such as Huntington's Disease, possession of one copy of the defective gene suffices to cause an individual to suffer from its ravages. However, an individual with only one copy of a gene associated with a genetically recessive disease will remain asymptomatic, but can transmit or 'carry' the defective gene to the next generation. Furthermore, in the case of some diseases, such as breast cancer, possession of the relevant gene does not guarantee that the individual will fall sick, but simply indicates that she is at an increased likelihood of doing so. Finally, even if the presence of a particular genetic defect virtually guarantees that a person will suffer from the associated disorder, it may not be conclusive about its severity or time of onset.

In the development of bioethics thus far, yeoman work has been done by the ideal of 'informed consent'. What role will that concept play in the complex and variegated world of genetic information? How does one give informed consent to the acquisition of unalterable knowledge about oneself without, in the first place, knowing what that information is? Should individuals have the same right to refuse life-altering genetic knowledge that they do to refuse a life-altering medical procedure? Furthermore, how should society view parents who have their minor children tested for an adult-onset disorder such as Huntington's Disease? Are they merely doing their job, enabling the child to accept and make wise decisions on the basis of her particular medical lot in life (which they may share themselves), just as they enable her to accept and make decisions in view of the intellectual and even economic resources that happen to be available to her? Or, on the other hand, is a genetic profile the sort of self-knowledge that should be discovered by the individual herself, rather than conveyed by others?

There are no simple answers to this set of questions. However, by attempting to address them in the familiar categories of autonomy and informed consent, contemporary bioethics sidesteps a crucial set of problems raised by contemporary genetics.[22]

III. The expressive force of the law

The issues considered in the previous two sections of this article concern the *negative* limits that should be placed on the pursuit and use of genetic knowledge. Ultimately, however, these limits will be persuasive only if they are situated within a broader *positive* vision about the meaning and purpose of our collective attempt to understand the human genome. Whether we like it or not, secular law will play a significant role in constructing the metaphors that Americans will use to understand themselves and their fellow citizens as both bound together and differentiated by similarities and differences in their DNA patterns.

An inchoate sense of the power that law exerts over the way in which we understand our relationships with one another lies behind the public brouhaha that developed over the patenting of genetically altered life forms. In 1995, almost two hundred leaders representing more than eighty religious faiths sought to do battle with the biotechnology industry by lending their signatures to a 'Joint Appeal Against Human and Animal Patenting', which was spearheaded by the radical environmental activist Jeremy Rifkin. The Joint Appeal objected to the 'patenting of human and animal life forms' on the grounds that they 'are creations of God, not humans, and as such should not be patented as human inventions'.[23]

The biotechnology industry mounted a vigorous response to the Joint Appeal; on purely pragmatic grounds, the industry representatives appeared to have the better of the argument. First, no one was claiming that a scientist could patent naturally occurring, unaltered genetic material. In order to obtain any patent, whether it has to do with genetic material or not, an applicant must show that the patented material is an *invention*, not a discovery of something occurring in the same form in nature. Second, a patent confers a relative, not an absolute property right on the patent holder. It does not give her the positive right to use and market the invention, it simply confers the negative right to exclude other persons from so doing without her permission for a limited length of time, usually twenty years. Consequently, patent law would not prevent state and federal governments from implementing laws designed to combat the dangers of biotechnology. Third, the patent system serves a socially beneficial purpose by encouraging investment in scientific progress in the expensive and uncertain area of biotechnology. It encourages prospective inventors and financiers by assuring them that no one will be able to 'steal' their hard-earned invention before they can recoup the fruits of their investment. Patents foster the free exchange of scientific knowledge by requiring inventors to make public disclosure sufficient to allow other persons skilled in the industry to replicate their inventions.

Some of the worries lying behind the Joint Appeal are based on a legitimate fear of the sinister side of the genetic revolution, which would remain a danger with or without patenting, as critics were quick to point out. Still other worries are likely grounded in a misunderstanding about the indispensable role played by intellectual property in our post-industrial society. However, it may also be that its signatories have identified a valid concern about the relationshp of *law* to contemporary genetics, albeit in a somewhat diffuse and confused way. This concern is likely to remain shadowy and insubstantial to those who understand the role of law in society solely in concrete, functional terms.[24] It comes into sharper focus if one recognizes, along with the legal theorist James Boyd White,[25] that law has a symbolic, constitutive function in society, shaping social character in a way that is not reducible to the narrow tracings of statutory requirements and judicial holdings.

A key feature of legal reasoning in the American common law system is its analogical quality. Concepts that find their initial home in one area of the law are frequently extended by analogy to an entirely different sphere, where they take root and begin to exert their influence. This phenomenon is at once a source of creativity and danger. We may forget that our use of a 'borrowed' concept is in fact analogous, and begin treating that concept as if it were as directly and straightforwardly applicable in its new legal context as in its original one. In other words, if we press useful, but limited, legal analogies too far, we may end up with a 'seepage' problem.

For example, American law has long treated corporations as legal persons which have an identity distinct from that of the individuals who founded them or currently control them. This legal fiction has facilitated commerce by allowing a valuable co-operative endeavour to endure through time, despite the inevitable changes in the personnel contributing to its success. However, in *First National Bank of Boston v. Bellotti*,[26] the United States Supreme Court arguably took the analogy too far. In *Bellotti*, the Court held that business corporations are persons with rights of free speech protected by the First Amendment to the Constitution. On that basis, it struck down a Massachusetts statute prohibiting such corporations from making political contributions with respect to any matters except those materially affecting their businesses. Ironically enough, by losing sight of the limited and analogous sense in which corporations can be viewed as persons, the Court substantially diluted the free speech rights of the actual human beings whom the category of personhood was originally designed to protect.

A fruitful way of reading the Joint Appeal is as a plea to avoid a *Bellotti*-like situation in the area of biotechnology; it is a call to reflect critically upon the interpretative framework that patent law is extending by analogy to recent genetic advances. There are at least two aspects of that framework that merit cautious consideration.

First, patent law is not directed toward theoretical understanding, but toward *practically useful knowledge*. In lay terms, patents safeguard innovative, valuable 'know-how' from commercial exploitation without the patent holder's consent. They do not protect discoveries of the way the natural world operates, no matter how brilliant; thus Albert Einstein could not have patented his theory of relativity. One consequence of allowing patent law to frame our new understanding of human genetics is that we may eventually come to perceive that field as offering us information that all responsible persons must in some way act upon, as soon as the appropriate technology is provided to us. Unfortunately, one day this perception might contribute to a social momentum that takes us too quickly beyond the more-or-less justifiable programmes of therapeutic genetic intervention in order to cure disease or ameliorate defects, and into the far more troublesome realm of engineering genetic improvements for individual persons or the entire human race.[27]

Second, and more generally, patent law orientates genetic information on the commercial market place, where it will become (and in some cases, already is) a valuable commodity. The market place can create perceived needs where none existed before (e.g., automobiles and telephones); it can also strongly affect the way in which naturally occurring needs are interpreted. Our understanding of adequate food and shelter, arguably the two goods for which we have the strongest natural requirements, is heavily influenced by market forces. Access to 'fast food' and indoor plumbing have become non-negotiable necessities to all but a small segment of the American population.

The concept of the human genome will play an important symbolic role in the constitution of our communities in the years to come. More specifically, our understanding of that concept will fundamentally shape our ideals of both a common human nature and the uniqueness of particular individuals, which are arguably as basic for our political life as food and shelter are for our biological life. If, from the very earliest stages of our discovery of the human genome, we permit patenting and other forms of commodification, then we may never have the opportunity collectively to work out its symbolic social meaning apart from the instrumental value it has in the marketplace. It will be as if we had no understanding of food against which to assess the claims made by McDonalds, and no understanding of shelter to serve as a reality check for the advertisements in *House & Garden*. It is hard to avoid the suspicion that the marginalized will be the losers as a result of this turn of events in the development of our understanding of the human genome. The middle and upper classes will spend their assets in order to meet their new genetic 'needs'; the poor will be left to the fickle wheel of the genetic lottery.

Conclusion

The United States is far from articulating, let alone implementing, a comprehensive ethical, legal and regulatory framework sufficient to deal with the challenges posed by the new genetics. Success or failure in developing such a framework in the coming years will in large part depend upon our willingness to rethink fundamental presuppositions regarding the nature of the human person, illness and death, the physician-patient relationship, and information and informed consent.

Bioethicists and health care policy analysts working within the Roman Catholic tradition may be well-positioned to contribute to the American debate on these matters. Catholic moralists have long stressed the essentially embodied and essentially social (in particular, familial) nature of the human person. We have always acknowledged the inevitability of illness and death in this life, along with the promise of immortality with Christ Jesus in the next one. We have access to a way of understanding vocations, including the medical vocation, in a broader context that can overcome the isolation of the physician-patient dyad. Finally, in our rich history of spiritual direction, we can find resources for understanding the strength that can come through self-knowledge, even if it is of an unwelcome sort. This is not, of course, to claim that the Catholic moral tradition can 'solve' the multifacted moral, social and political issues raised by contemporary genetics. It is, however, to hope that by drawing upon the resources of our heritage with well-mixed parts of creativity and humility, Catholics may help illuminate the most significant biomedical issue at the beginning of the third millennium.

Notes

1. National Bioethics Advisory Commission, *Cloning Human Beings: Report and Recommendations of the National Bioethics Advisory Commission*, Rockville, MD, June 1997.

2. In the United States, the HGP is principally funded by the National Institutes of Health, the Department of Energy, and the Howard Hughes Medical Institute. Its two-pronged goal is to 'map' the location of approximately 80,000 genes on the 46 chromosomes of the human genome, and sequence the nearly 6 billion DNA nucleotides that form the building blocks of those chromosomes. The HGP expects to achieve this goal by the year 2005.

3. The best article I have come across on the paradigm shifts that will be required as a result of the new genetics is Albert R. Jonsen, 'The Impact of Mapping the Human Genome on the Patient-Physician Relationship', in Thomas H. Murray, Mark A. Rothstein and Robert F. Murray, Jr (eds), *The Human Genome Project and the Future of Health Care*, Bloomington, IN 1996, 1–20.

4. *Code of Federal Regulations*, vol. 45, part 46.

5. There is some hope that this *laissez-faire* attitude at the federal level might change; Senator John Glenn has introduced a bill into Congress entitled the 'Human Research Subject Protections Act of 1997', which would subject *all* experimentation involving human subjects to follow informed consent protocols and submit to the scrutiny of institutional review boards.

6. For example, when deciding the famous 'Baby M' case in 1988, the New Jersey Supreme Court held that surrogate motherhood contracts were unenforceable because against public policy. Nothing in the decision, however, prevents couples seeking to hire a surrogate mother from doing so. *In the Matter of Baby M*, 109 NJ 396 (1988). Recognizing that the courts will not come to their aid if the arrangement turns sour, such couples could simply decide to take their chances and solicit the services of a surrogate motherhood.

7. In making its appropriations for fiscal year 1997, Congress continued to ban the use of federal funds to support the creation of human embryos for research purposes, or to support research in which embryos are destroyed, discarded, or knowingly subjected to risk of injury or death greater than that allowed under the applicable regulations pertaining to research on human foetuses.

8. The Fertility Clinic Success Rate and Certification Act of 1992, US Code vol. 42, secs. 263a–1 et seq. covers all laboratories and treatments entailing manipulation of human embryos and eggs. It requires such facilities to report statistics on the number of pregnancies achieved to the Department of Health and Human Services (DHHS), and directs DHHS to develop a model programme for inspection and certification of fertility clinics, which would be implemented by the states.

9. Sheryl Stolberg, 'Reproductive Research Far Outpaces Public Policy', *Los Angeles Times*, 29 April 1997.

10. Germ line therapy is the alteration of the genetic structure of the reproductive cells of an individual, to prevent her from passing a genetic disorder on to her offspring.

11. See Mary Ann Bobinski, 'Genetics and Reproductive Decision Making', in *The Human Genome Project and the Future of Health Care* (n. 3), 133–57.

12. The best discussion of the current state and future prospect of gene therapy is: LeRoy Walters and Julie Gage Palmer, *The Ethics of Human Gene Therapy*, New York 1997.

13. In the background, of course, is the menacing spectre of eugenics. This is a concept which has taken root and flourished in American soil in the past. Its zenith was reached in a Supreme Court opinion by Justice Oliver Wendel Holmes, upholding a state law mandating the sterilization of mentally retarded persons. His exact words, so shocking to us now, were 'three generations of imbeciles are enough'. *Buck v. Bell*, 274 US 200, 207 (1927).

14. See, e.g., John A. Robertson, 'The Potential Impact of the Human Genome Project on Procreative Liberty', in George J. Annas and Sherman Elias (eds), *Gene Mapping: Using Law and Ethics as Guides*, New York 1992, 215–25, and Mary Anne Bobinski, 'Genetics and Reproductive Decision Making' (n.11).

15. See, e.g., US Congress, House, Genetic Confidentiality and Nondiscrimination Act of 1996, 104th Cong. 2nd Sess. S. 1898.

16. Health Insurance Portability and Accountability Act of 1996, *US Code*, vol. 42, secs. 201 *et seq.*

17. Americans With Disbilities Act of 1990, *US Code*, vol. 42, secs. 12101 *et seq.*

18. See, e.g., Adrienne Asch, 'Genetics and Employment: More Disability Discrimination', in *The Human Genome Project* (n. 3), 158–72.

19. See, e.g., Roberta M. Berry, 'The Human Genome Project and the End of Insurance', *University of Florida Journal of Law and Public Policy* 7, 1996, 205–56 and Robert J. Pokorski, 'Use of Genetic Information by Private Insurers', in Timothy F. Murphy and Marc A. Lappé (eds), *Justice and the Human Genome Project*, Berkeley 1994, 91–109.

20. For example, under the landmark ruling in *Tarasoff v. Regents of the University of California*, 13 Cal. 3rd 177 (1974), the California Supreme Court held that a psychiatrist has a duty to warn a third person when he realizes that such a warning is essential to prevent his patient from inflicting physical harm on that patient.

21. See John C. Fletcher and Dorothy C. Wertz, 'Ethics, Law, and Medical Genetics: After the Human Genome is Mapped', *Emory Law Journal* 39, 1990, 747–809. This article surveys the response of genetic counsellors to this and other moral dilemmas.

22. See Dena Davis, 'Genetic Dilemmas and the Child's Right to an Open Future', *Hastings Center Report* 17:2, 1997, 7–15.

23. The Catholic signatories to the document included a collection of prelates that would be the envy of the Common Ground Initiative founded by the late Joseph Cardinal Bernardin, including William Levada, Raymond Lucker, Francis Stafford and Rembert Weakland.

24. David B. Resnik, 'The Morality of Human Gene Patents', *Kennedy Institute of Ethics Journal* 7:1, 1997, 43–61.

25. See James Boyd White, *Heracles' Bow: Essay on the Rhetoric and Poetics of Law*, Madison, WI 1985.

26. *First National Bank of Boston v. Bellotti*, 435 US 765 (1977).

27. As many commentators have pointed out, we cannot draw a sharp line between therapeutic genetic interventions (i.e., interventions designed to cure defects) and interventions aimed at enhancing human capabilities; nonetheless, the general distinction is still useful.

Power, Ethics and the Poor in Human Genetic Research

Márcio Fabri dos Anjos

Genetics is today recognized as a field in which the quest for knowledge and power has been concentrated. In the areas of crop cultivation and animal husbandry, its achievements have brought about a real revolution, not only in terms of food production, but also, thanks to recent advances, leading to new pharmaceutical products and even to organic elements that can be transplanted into humans. Researches in human genetics have formed part of this expansion of knowledge of biological processes, with a corresponding expansion in the power to control them. Here knowledge brings health and well-being, while at the same time increasingly promising to extend human power to programme life itself. This shows the truth of the axiom that 'knowledge is power', and knowledge and power, once joined, tend to empower each other, in a spiral of interraction.[1]

Among the many ethical questions raised by this subject, I should like to raise the place of the poor in human genetic research. What chances do countries, populations, groups and individuals lacking the resources to acquire genetic knowledge have of sharing in the research and benefiting from its results? Defining this question as an ethical concern, I propose to raise a few interrogatives from the perspective of the poor and also to sketch out proposals on proceedings in power relationships in this area.[2]

I. Powers and interests at stake

In general, and without for the moment considering current tensions, the course of research into human genetics holds out most promise in the areas of health, longevity and quality of life. At the same time, these objectives are tied up with a chain of more pragmatic interests that result in the commercialization of the results obtained, whether services or products. It is worth noting that the mapping and sequencing of genes brings new resources for identifying and assessing human individuals, intervening in their procreation, diagnosing hereditary diseases, preventing sicknesses, and bringing the possibility of genetic therapies.

These illustrations are enough to show the considerable political and economic potential wrapped up in human genetic research. We are generating a power to intervene in the very biological identity of persons, their prospects and chances of life. It is therefore easy to see why human genetics has become a field attracting huge financial investment, with strong prospects of large profits. The news media detail the vast sums involved in the economic aspects of this field: research with genetic materials is 'the latest frontier in science – and a market that promises to generate billions of dollars. The first vast contract has already been signed. The US corporation Sequana Therapeutics claims to have found the cure for asthma in an African coastal tribe. It has sold DNA samples from this group to Boehringer, a German pharmaceutical laboratory, for US$ 70 million. None of the blacks involved has earned a cent from this operation.'[3] This little example shows that genetics has become a field of economic and political endeavour that national and international policies cannot ignore. It is no longer just a case of applying the results of research to individuals, but of rapidly accumulating options that can affect the whole of humanity.

Two interrelated forces constitute the requisite for entering this area of knowledge and power. In effect, the way to achieving results in genetic research has a long history of high monetary cost and highly developed scientific resources. Researchers have to be trained, research centres established, and projects financed. Those with the economic and scientific potential to do this can produce in genetics and enter into the developing competition, seeking to lead the race and capture the market. Those who lack this potential may be in the position of satisfying the requirements to become consumers of the results if and when these become available.

Those who have the economic and scientific potential to develop research and furnish its results fall into two main groups: on the one hand, the public authorities of various countries, concerned with the development of health programmes for their own populations, as well as with the economic exploitation of the services and products resulting from research; on the other, private initiatives, composed mainly of pharmaceutical industries and medical and health bodies, which seek to make human genetics a profitable enterprise for themselves on a national and a multinational level.

Beyond these, there are those dispossessed of the necessary potential to produce in genetics. On the present map of geo-power in genetics, the North is significantly stronger than the South. Economically poor countries (with a few exceptions, such as Cuba, which has made a special investment in public health), most of the black populations, and indigenous peoples in a general sense have no chance of leading in any initiatives taken in these fields.

II. Vulnerability and autonomy

As can be seen, the question of ethics in power relationships in human genetics is posed within a context of great economic inequality and of corresponding differentials in capacity for scientific production. I am not going to go over the ethical interrogatives hanging over the free-market economics dominant in the West, though these form an important underlying context to this study. Here I am less concerned with analysing the competition, the play of forces and pressures among the 'strong'. I prefer to concentrate on the situation of the dispossessed in the midst of these power relationships.

Vulnerability is an interesting concept in bioethics insofar as it expresses the situation of those with limited capacity for autonomy and for defending their own rights in questions of research and of profiting from its results. Vulnerability is generally assessed by the limits to the capacity people have for taking decisions freely. It is well established that this capacity can be diminished or even annulled by the absence of conditions of understanding, culture and feeling (where the vulnerable include children, comatose patients, and those with no access to even a minimum knowledge of scientific procedures). The vulnerable would also include individuals subject to certain pressures, especially when subordinated to a hierarchy, such as the military and members of any institution that can exercise pressure. Perhaps less recognized are those whose vulnerability stems from economic pressures and from exploitation of situations that leaves them with few alternatives. Understanding these levels of vulnerability becomes easier when illustrated with some specific examples.

1. *Lack and the attraction of promise*

The Brazilian newspaper report on 'sale of indigenous DNA'[4] is instructive for understanding some aspects of vulnerability. The paper related that the Coriell Cell Repositories Corporation, in the United States, was in 1996 offering for sale samples of DNA from two Brazilian indigenous groups, the Karitiana and the Surui, both from the State of Rondônia in Amazonia. On its Internet page (//www.arginine. umdnj.edu), Coriell mentioned that the samples came from the collections of two prestigious US universities, Stanford and Yale, and that the Yale doctor Ken Kidd had handed over the samples. Among the economic data provided was the statement that 'Coriell Cell calls itself a scientific concern, with no profit aims. It charges $500 for each DNA sample', but this amount barely covers the cost of collecting and processing.

The declaration by the village headman on the manner of collecting the samples is also revealing on the subject of vulnerability. According to the same report, in August 1996 researchers from the United States obtained authorization from *FUNAI* (the National Foundation for Indians) for research into the Giant Sloth in Karatiana territory. In the words of the headman Cizino Dantas Morais, the collection of samples took place like this: 'When we went into the jungle to show them the lair of the mapinguari (the legendary 'sloth-beast'), doctor asked Karitiana for blood. They said: we are going to see if you have anaemia, meningitis, AIDS, disease that kills quickly. Indian let them take blood.' The reporter concluded by saying that the Karitiana have not the least idea of what DNA is, but have now discovered that their blood is worth money: 'After finding out that their blood is on sale in the United States, they want money from any researcher who comes to collect blood on their territory.'

2. *Patients who have never had treatment*

The relationshp between lack and promises of benefit shows that vulnerability is also defined by exploitation of those who find themselves in situations where they have few alternatives. In poor regions, there are innumerable 'patients who have never had treatment', who are quite beyond the reach of public health networks. For these, becoming subjects in a research project seems like a guarantee of salvation. Recently a many-centred research project on the efficacy of a drug to combat AIDS, 'the largest research into medicaments to combat AIDS undertaken outside the USA and Europe, involving 996 Brazilian volunteers', applied a monotherapic treatment to HIV-positive patients who had never had any treatment, to evaluate the efficacy of the drug (Indinavir). Now, as far as one can tell, the scientific community maintains the inefficacy of monotherapy in such cases. The American laboratory Merk Sharp & Dohme, which financed the project, confronted by a commission for ethics in research which raised ethical questions, suspended this branch of research.[5]

I am not passing ethical judgment here on the actions of this laboratory. But I mention the incident to show how understandable it is that an HIV-carrier's need for treatment can become a weak point that is easily exploited. In truth, this personal vulnerability is not isolated and simply the outcome of the patient's psychological state. It is connected with a broader weakness affecting society, which is supposed to protect individuals. Note that those 'who had never had any treatment' were sought out. This means that, to the extent that societies are incapable of defending those who suffer, or simply uncaring, they increase their vulnerability. So countries with precarious health systems and few rules governing research are always oases, not always ethical, open to those who have the economic and scientific potential to carry out research.

3. The vulnerability of nations

I have already mentioned the vulnerability of indigenous peoples. Let us now look closer at the question of national sovereignty of countries with poor populations. A first aspect of weakness appears when a nation lacks a minimum of directives and resources to control research proceedings. The condition of many poor countries can be called calamitous in this regard, which in itself makes it difficult to name the countries with such limitations. In recent discussions on biomedical ethics with a view to signing treaties within Mercosul ('south trade'), it was found that some South American countries had (in 1996) no such thing as a Code of Medical Ethics. How, in such a situation, can one propose an ethics of research? It is easy to see how, in such a context, individuals are defenceless against those who have power without ethics.

The question of national sovereignty surfaced in acute fashion in researches into the Amazon rainforest.[6] The US laboratory Sharman Pharmaceuticals alone has investigated around 7,000 plant species from the Amazonian region. This major research project necessarily involves national sovereignty, both when the research is carried out and at the time when its results are patented and start earning royalties. The Royal Botanical Gardens of the United Kingdom, considering the question of rights on eventual discoveries a delicate matter, suspended its researches into the production of remedies based on Brazilian plants.[7] At the Rio ECO-92 Conference, a Convention on Biodiversity was signed, providing for the payment of royalties to the community or country of origin on products that utilize indigenous community knowledge or native raw materials.[8]

However, regulating research in poor countries is still not everything. Another aspect of national vulnerability is shown directly in international political and economic relationships, in which rights recognized can be subjected to various pressures and have to be negotiated. One example of this emerges from the laws governing patents. Regulation in this sphere is absolutely necessary, beginning with the need to defend not only nations but also businesses from bio-piracy. But this does not save regulation from being subject to a powerful play of interests. In Brazil, policy negotiations began in 1991 and took five years, ending by recognizing patents on genetically modified micro-organisms and conceding a validity of twenty years for patents on products manufactured from them. Now, given the increasing rate of change in all aspects of life today, twenty years can correspond to a hundred in earlier times. A concession as generous as this is inexplicable without political and economic pressures, a context of free-market ideology, and the need to attract foreign capital into the country.

III. Deconstruction and construction of ethics in research

What can be concretely postulated in terms of ethics, especially in societies or countries lacking in the relevant social regulation? Does one begin with norms or with laws? I am convinced there is an earlier step. Laws and norms will become necessary, but they depend on establishing a more solid ethical and cultural base if they are not to fall into legalism.

The first concern, therefore, has to be to dismantle a colonist mentality, and replace it with an ethical culture, informed by humanitarian convictions and invested with citizenship. I speak on the basis of the Latin American colonial experience: in other contexts the experience may be more imperialist or dictatorial, but the experiences are relatively analogous. The remnants of colonial culture have the effect of making territories and peoples 'no man's land', open ground for the first explorer to arrive to operate in with no rules other than those he makes himself. The force of inertia in this culture still persists today, imbuing many researchers with the omnipotence of not having to give satisfaction to their patients or subjects for research. A dictatorial context would treat territory and people as 'one man's land', with the same practical results.

We can point to two reciprocal dimensions of this process that need to be reversed. One shows in the interpersonal relations between researchers and the subjects of their research. In these, both researchers and their subjects need to learn ethical attitudes, to discover and respect the dignity of those involved in the relationship. The other concerns the socio-political sphere, affecting public state relationships. Here it is not just a question of respecting individual rights but of claiming and defending the rights of the collectivity. An interesting example of this dimension is provided by the projected Law of Biodiversity approved in the state of Acre, one of the states that make up Brazilian Amazonia. By this law, researchers or foreign entities that propose to work in the region have to be associated with a Brazilian group; besides this, they have to leave part of the material they collect behind, in the hands of the state. The deputy responsible for this project commented emphatically: 'The time has come to put a stop once and for all to the neo-colonialism attacking Acre and the whole region of Amazonia.'[9]

Are these harsh judgments? Or do they just appear harsh simply because we have always counted on the compliance of colonialism? Once knowledge becomes power, overcoming colonialism and dependency means sharing knowledge itself, not just handing on its products. In other words, ethics in research is not upheld simply by interpersonal relations of respect between researcher and subject of research. We need to have the courage to confront also the tacit laws of the political, economic and cultural colonialism to which most poor countries are still subject.

The cultural construction of an ethics in research refers us, as we have seen, to the foundations of our human inter-connectedness. On the one hand, it requires us to strengthen our consciousness of the humanitarian commitments that unite us as like beings. On the other, it demands a sort of cosmic vision, a 'galaxy view', forcing us to accept that as planet Earth we are a tiny boatload navigating the expanse of the universe. The spirit of solidarity with and sharing of the planet, and therefore among nations, would be a basic rule of common sense.

As we well know, on the other hand, society is hardly governed by ethical ideals. So, laws and directives are needed. In building an ethical construct, norms and directives are often more appropriate than laws. Laws suppose sanctions and punishment; they involve enforcement officers; they lead to more directly juridical proceedings – which are obviously needed in certain cases. But directives and norms seem more effective in developing ethical formation and consolidating attitudes. The growth of the ethical consciousness of humanity on this subject has been marked by significant occasions, on which important international declarations were signed, setting out directives for ethics in research. Notable, among others, are the *Nüremberg Code* (1947), the *UN Declaration on Human Rights* (1948), the *Helsinki Declaration* (1964 and later versions), the *UN International Agreement on Civil and Political Rights* (1966), the *CIOMS/OMS Proposals for International Ethical Directives for Biomedical Research involving Human Beings* (1982, 1993), and the *CIOMS International Directives for the Ethical Control of Epimediological Studies* (1991).

While, therefore, there are still motives for deploring the lack of ethics in many research proceedings, there are also, on the other hand, reasons to rejoice at these expressions of ethical maturity on the part of global society.

IV. Ethics in day-to-day research

In day-to-day research practices, ethics is well regulated by norms proposed or upheld by local and national committees of research ethics. There is an accessible bibliography on the functioning of such committees.[10] There are two distinct, though related, undertakings: working out national norms or directives governing ethics in research, and forming commissions or committees to implement them. In Brazil, the first of these appeared in the 1960s, but took definite shape in the 1970s as 'Committees for Hospital Ethics'.[11] After this, local committees and national commissions with a broader remit began to be formed. Ethical concern is undoubtedly growing throughout the world, and it is to be hoped that all countries will soon organize the institution of these valuable bodies for promoting ethics.

What steps are needed to regulate the ethics of research, and what must such regulation comprise? In the Brazilian experience, in 1996, of reworking a National Resolution on *Ethics in Research involving Human Beings*,[12] we found that it was vital to begin with a democratic process for formulating directives, involving society in the actual elaboration of suitable norms. In such cases, participation is a potent factor in ethical education. So it is useful to organize a collection of suggestions, proposals and observations in which various sectors of society can take part. It is essential for research centres themselves to contribute, and interdisciplinary contributions are also very enriching.

The next stage is to plumb the ethical heritage of humankind. At first sight, the search for consensus would seem to be the next logical step after collecting contributions. But consensus can sometimes, to a greater or lesser extent, express the simple agreement of the strongest, and this is no guarantee of an ethical procedure. To counterbalance this disadvantage, one needs to be able to incorporate the experiences and ethical expressions of international agreements and the experiences of other countries. Contexts in which more humanitarian and egalitarian models of relationship in research have already been established can serve not only as an inspiration in drawing up norms but also as a policy instrument in overcoming imbalances and inequalities in the situation in one's own country.

The content of regulations for ethics in research will necessarily be complex in detail, and they can therefore be more conveniently adopted from regulations worked out in the various countries that already have them. Their principal tasks have to be: to include ethics in the scientific process itself; to require that the maximum of respect be shown for the subjects of research, paying particular attention to their 'free and informed consent';[13] to establish guarantees on risks and benefits; to ensure a structure of openness in research, in its installation, development and conclusion;[14] to establish a national commission and local committees for ethics, which can put the necessary directives into practice.

Finally, it needs to be said that day-to-day ethics in human genetics inevitably refers us to the broader socio-political conditions under which research takes place and under which the results it obtains are distributed and applied. I have mentioned some of these, but description and analysis of the ethical questions raised by this subject have been reserved to another contributor in this volume. Here, I must just note the need for regulations and laws that deal with more than the research process, protecting the ethical application of the results obtained. So poor countries, too, need good laws on biodiversity, bioprotection, patents, applications of therapies and especially of diagnosis. Defence of the poor and upholding the dignity of the vulnerable depend very largely on these legal dispositions.

Conclusion

In conclusion, I should like to return to the question of the place of the poor in human genetic research. It is obvious that the course of research in this field involves colossal economic and political interests and therefore sets a complex interplay of forces in motion. Scientific progress depends on effort and the investment of energy and also relies on the attraction of the benefits and profits it can bring. The poor, as individuals, groups, or nations, are, in this interplay, an ethical challenge remaining present from the installation of research projects and throughout the whole process of their development, in both their methods of procedure and the use they make of their results. At each of these stages there are vulnerable and dispossessed persons requiring respect and needing signs of solidarity.

How effective can such a challenge be in the face of power play? First, it is right to recognize humankind's capacity for producing ethics, however profound the ambiguities we experience. Human power is not corrupt for being power, but through the lack of commitment with which it is invoked in relationships with our fellows.

Second, the poor have considerable allies in those who are using their power in research in an ethical manner, and also in those who are working for human rights in all sectors affected by human genetic research. In the end, however, the effectiveness of the ethical challenge posed by the poor depends on the poor themselves growing in consciousness of their dignity and of their social rights and responsibilities. It is also fundamental to add that the poor come into ethics as agents and co-workers, not needing to remain in their customary condition of recipients of compassion. In the research field, there are signs that social organizations are moving in this direction in the so-called Third World. And once the poor and vulnerable are no longer trampled on in this power play, humanity will have become more human. And would this not be one of the most important criteria for measuring real progress in human genetics?

Translated by Paul Burns

Notes

1. A. Toffler, *Powershift: The Overthrow of the Elites*, 1990.

2. I should like to express special thanks to L. Pessini, vice director of the S. Camilo Integrated Faculties, São Paulo, for his valuable help in this study.

3. M. C. Carvalho, 'Firm sells indigenous DNA', in *Folha S. Paulo*, 1 June 1997.

4. Ibid.

5. Pivetta, 'Ethical committee suspends AIDS research', in *Folha S. Paulo*, 22 March 1997.

6. 'The world market in remedies derived from plants is now approaching $32 billion, according to UN estimates', *Folha S. Paulo*, 6 July 1997.

7. J. C. Assumpçao, 'Forest becomes pharmacy', in *Folha S. Paulo*, 1 June 1997.

8. It is not in the least surprising that the United States refused to take part in this Convention.

9. *Folha S. Paulo*, 6 July 1997.

10. In view of the difficulty of compiling a bibliography accessible to all language areas in which this volume is published, I note merely: W. T. Reich (ed.), 'Research Ethics Committee', in *Encyclopedia of Bioethics*, New York, ²1995; D. P. Salas, 'Estructura y función de los Comités de Etica de la Investigación Clínica', in *Cuadernos del Programa Regional de Bioética*, Chile, OPAS/OMS, 1996, 3, 92–105.

11. C. A. Mühlen, 'Comitês de Etica em Pesquisa em Seres Humanos nos Estados Unidos da Amêrica', in *Bioética*, Brasilia-DF 1993, 3, 45.

12. Ministry of Health, National Health Council, doc. 01960/96.

13. The *vulnerable* subjects, mentioned above, deserve special consideration here..

14. The Brazilian Resolution establishes a protocol containing the following elements in its description of research: 'detailed financial budget for the research'; guarantee that 'the results of the research will be made public'; 'declaration of the use and destination of material and/or data collected'; description of the procedure to be followed in obtaining 'free and informed consent'.

IV · Theological Perspectives

First Sheep, then Human Beings? Theological and Ethical Reflections on the Use of Gene Technology

Eberhard Schockenhoff

The development of modern gene technology makes it possible for human beings to go beyond limits which were established in the previous course of their history. As long as the scope of their scientific and technical activity on nature was limited by nature itself, the question of the legitimation of such interventions did not yet arise with the acuteness which it now has. We must ask about the human significance of limits which were formerly imposed by nature, and in religion, ethics and law look for sustainable foundations on which to establish new limits. What technology can do does not automatically satisfy the criterion of ethical responsibility and what is humanly desirable.

I. Limits of nature – limits of ethics?

Biblical creation faith reminds human beings both of their commission to rule and of the special position which this gives them among all creatures, and also of their inalienable responsibility for the well-being of the whole of creation, which accrues to them precisely as a result of their exalted role as God's representatives and governors. Their charge to shape creation and their place among the creatures thus belong inseparably together: on the basis of the similarity of all creation to its divine origin, nature too gains a part in the reverence which human beings should feel towards their transcendent Creator. But in so far as nature not only reflects the beauty and glory of the triune God and the divine fullness of life but at the same time is distorted as a result of the breach caused by sin, in the form which it in fact has it cannot simply be identified with the divine will for the creation.

If at the same time according to the biblical understanding the origin of evil is not to be sought in a negative principle of the world or in the dark aspects of the deity, but in a contingent state of freedom which refers back to the first beginnings of human history, the consequences of evil materialize in the structures of the fallen creation. They are tangible in the destructive forces and the disruptive tendencies which threaten both the life of human beings and animals and inanimate nature in the form of diseases, accidents and catastrophes. Because creation is always also the place where evil breaks in and never exists only in the undisturbed reflection of its divine origin, according to the biblical understanding, in principle human interventions are allowed to sustain nature and make it useful; theologically they must be understood as collaboration with the divine action in creation. Since the limits of such interventions in an evolutionary dynamic picture of the world cannot be read off existing ordinances of nature, they must be rediscovered and recognized through being opened up by human reason. That there must be such limits follows from the finitude of human beings and the limitations of their constitution. However, precisely where these limits run cannot be discovered in advance of the state of possibilities of scientific and technological intervention at any one time. Rather, critical reflection is needed on the conditions and consequences of human action which investigates what technology is capable of at any time on the basis of what is reasonable for human beings. Thus scientific self-control and ethical reflection are called for to define afresh the limits within which science and research, medicine and gene technology, serve human well-being.

The criterion of human dignity, respect for the life of others, and the prohibition against killing, give us important criteria for forming ethical judgments which make it possible to define the first limits in situations of conflict in bioethics. Common to all these criteria is that they formulate only a *negative* restriction, and not as yet any comprehensive aim. They describe the limiting conditions on human action in the borderland between life and death.

Below this level, at which the claim of the person is expressed in negative obligations relating to what is not to be done, we need further ethical criteria of evaluation so that we can assess particular research projects in gene technology and the procedures used in them. Here above all we must consider the justification for the aims and the responsibility for the consequences; this must precede or accompany individual research projects. In connection with the present possibilities of using gene technology on human beings, here we shall investigate the opportunities for forming an ethical judgment by means of two examples. In one case (genetic diagnosis) the ethical reflection tends to be retrospective and to go along with scientific progress, whereas in the other case (cloning) the future effect of its possibilities is anticipated.

II. The right not to know

In principle, the judgment to be made on the methods of prenatal diagnosis is no different from that on the procedures of medical investigation known so far. The ethical problems associated with it are not limited to the danger of a miscarriage or damage to the embryo in connection with taking tissue, although this risk attaching to intervention must also be included in the assessment and in the counselling of the parents, since in the invasive procedures practised at present the risk of damage is approximately equal to that in the diagnosis of a disruption of chromosomes (in amniocentesis it is between 0.5 and 1%, in chorion biopsy between 2 and 4%). The real problem in antenatal diagnostic procedures lies in the practical consequences of their application. It is the medical aim of prenatal diagnosis to recognize at an early stage developmental damage with a probable or (in conditions with a monogenetic cause) certain prognosis, in order to dispel any existing anxieties of parents and make possible the best medical care both for the mother and for the unborn child. In more than 97% of all cases the prenatal diagnosis leads to a negative finding; thus in numerous pregnancies in which there is a risk, it can make it easier to accept the child and thus prevent the pregnancies being terminated because of the vague fear of possible chromosome damage to it.

The ethical dilemma to which the use of prenatal diagnostic procedures can lead becomes evident in the relatively rare cases in which the prenatal test predicts a genetic anomaly in the child. As long as there are only a few established medical therapies and the operative techniques are still at an early experimental stage, the diagnosis of a risk of genetic damage exposes the parents to the pressure of expectations in a mentality where the thought of abortion is widespread, a pressure which only a few find the courage to resist. The ethically legitimate desire for a healthy child and the medical aim of avoiding hereditary illnesses then lead to the decision to have an abortion being taken as an obvious consequence on medical grounds, and being derived from a catalogue of supposed forms of damage to the embryo.

According to a view which nowadays is largely taken for granted, the care of a handicapped child and life with it call for more personal readiness for sacrifice than law and morality can ask of the individual. This presupposition, backed by an uninvestigated consensus in society, is evidence of a deep inner contradiction which underlies the possibilities of prenatal diagnosis and genetic counselling of families. Whereas from a medical perspective the aim of this counselling is to be able to recognize and treat ailments in the developing child as early as possible, the secret expectation in society is one of the increasing suppression of the birth of handicapped children in the future with the aid of the diagnostic techniques of molecular biology. If prenatal diagnosis can be extended to an increasing number of ailments or even to genetic characteristics with only a small element of disease, this will also encourage the further development of eugenic tendencies in the population. Even now, in surveys on the question more than 40% of those surveyed say that they regard a genetic disposition to excess weight as sufficient indication for a precautionary termination of pregnancy.

The routine use of general screening procedures can lead to a change in the assessment of handicap and illness in the consciousness of the population and a tendency to regard any deviation from 'normality' as an intolerable limitation. To the degree that medicine is expected to fulfil the hope of the birth of a healthy child, and the diagnostic procedures of molecular biology are understood as sure 'guarantees' of this, the social resistance to and discrimination against the handicapped will increase. There is unmistakably less readiness to accept handicapped children and see them as a lifelong task which can bring not only limitations and burdens but also enrichment of one's own life.

Since the limits of one's own strength cannot be assessed in advance with any certainty, and the actual degree to which burdens can be tolerated depends very much on the personal attitude which parents develop even before the birth of their child, early knowledge of a risk of illness weakens the capacity to accept a handicapped child in the same way as a healthy child which at first sight seems more to satisfy the wishes of its parents. Moreover, the inability to imagine life with a handicapped child in the tangible burdens on everyday life as a serious alternative is reinforced by anxieties about public reactions. There is a fear that later one will have to justify oneself before society for the mere existence of a handicapped child, the acceptance of which one could have spared oneself and the community. Whereas formerly, after the chance birth of a handicapped child, parents could still count on the sympathy of neighbours, friends and relatives, in future they will increasingly come up against misunderstanding and rejection as a result of their decision voluntarily to accept a child which could also have remained unborn.

Even if such dangers of misuse, which are extremely difficult to control, do not rule out prenatal diagnosis, they must not be banished from social awareness. From an ethical perspective, there needs to be strict observance of three limits in particular which threaten to be forgotten in the uncontrolled use of investigative techniques based on molecular biology. In principle, prenatal diagnosis may be used only within the framework of medical questions: the discovery of general characteristics like gender, phenotypic characteristics or even psychological dispositions, should this ever be possible with a sufficiently certain prognosis, are ethically indefensible. Even if genetic tests had to be offered to all parents, no one should be forced actually to take them. Even the use of such prenatal diagnosis when indicated medically needs the assent of the parents, which can be given only after a comprehensive explanation of the risks of a miscarriage or damage to the child, and the moral conflicts which would arise were the finding to be positive. Even a refusal to employ prenatal diagnosis is ethically defensible. Indeed it calls for especial respect and esteem, where there are no clear signs of a substantial genetic handicap in the family. The special ethical value of such an attitude lies, first, in a protest against an illusory assignation of tasks to modern medicine, and secondly, in the readiness which it indicates to recognize human life without reservations, without subjecting it to a discriminatory assessment.

III. The right to natural birth and genetic chance

If human interventions in nature are in principle legitimate, then the cloning of animals cannot be objectionable simply because it goes beyond the limits which have applied so far. Nor can the novelty of the procedure be the basis for a categorical prohibition. However, because there is a need to preserve the multiplicity of species and respect the intrinsic value of animals, the fact that cloning is permissible in principle must not be understood as an unlimited authorization which legitimates the use of cloned animals for any purpose that is desirable from a human perspective. The techniques of splitting embryos which have been tested recently, or the transplantation of nuclei into previously denucleated embryonic cells from which their own genetic material has been removed, can only be justified in any balance between the benefits and the animal's own interests where from a human perspective it can be said that the goals of research are important and that the interests in terms of health are particularly urgent.

Among the conceivable fields in which cloning can be used in the foreseeable future and in which human beings can meaningfully make use of cloned animals, it will be necessary to make different ethical judgments depending on the particular aim. There is doubtless greater justification for so-called 'gene farming', which is meant to guarantee a consistent quality of drugs and important pharmaceutical substances, and for the transference of animal organs to human beings, than there is for an unlimited extension of the quantity of high-quality meat production, once that has been achieved, which is solely in the human interest. Since the animals of which human beings make use also have a creaturely value of their own over and above the functions which they fulfil, in the future, too, they should be preserved in all their genetic multiplicity and not be reduced to the function of cloned high-yielding species, bioreactors which can be reproduced at will and be substitutes for pharmaceutical machines.

By contrast, the cloning of human beings, should that ever prove successful, is incompatible with the notion of the personal dignity and individual purpose of each human being. The applications which are hoped for from a transference of cloning techniques to human beings – at present mention is made, for example, of improved methods of treating sterility, the avoidance of genetic hereditary diseases in families at risk, the possibility of multiplying the best transplant material for organ donors at will – are in part defined as medical research interests of great importance, which it can be ethically legitimate to pursue. However, in other cases the aims mentioned cannot be justified, nor are the consequences expected responsible. This is true in particular of the fantastic speculations about the infinite revival of dead human geniuses or the replication of individuals who are regarded as outstanding for the multiplication of twins at different times or an increase in the production of embryos within the framework of embryonic research.

Independently of the question whether the applications mentioned can be legitimate at the level of goals, the cloning of a human being must already be regarded as intrinsically reprehensible. An individual who came into being in this way would not be wanted for its own sake; it would be produced only as a means to an alien end. To force someone else's genetic identity on a person and to want to multiply someone because of the properties, capabilities or characteristics to which his or her genomes disposed him or her amounts to a clearly recognizable instrumentalization which is incompatible with human dignity and the notion that the human beings are an end in themselves. A human being who is to be brought to life only as a genetically appropriate organ donor, as a replacement for a spouse who has died prematurely, or as a reduplicated twin of its parents' eagerly awaited only child, could not exist as an end in himself or herself: such a person would have been affirmed only for a purpose external to his or her interests and would be accepted by those around only because his or her genetic characteristics served a particular purpose. Since the mere decision to produce such a person was made only for an alien purpose or to achieve the aim of a third party, from the first moment of his or her existence he or she would be deprived of the possibility of leading a life which had not been lived before and of being respected in an identity which was not under anyone's control and in this sense was 'fortuitous'. In analogy to the right to ignorance which human beings have, so that they cannot be forced to know the risks to life inherent in their genetic and biological make-up, in view of the future possibilities of a series of multiplications of the human genome, a right to individual fortuitousness must be postulated which protects the human being from the planned intervention of his or her procreators.

Here the crucial issue is not just that a human being has control over the genome of another, or that a number of human individuals share one and the same genetic make-up. The personal individuality and inalienable uniqueness of a human being do not end in his or her genetic programming: rather, the development of personal identity takes place in the process of an open interchange between natural disposition and environment which is only partially determined by the basic genetic programme. Therefore the human genome cannot be seen as the exclusive vehicle of the personal identity of a human being. However, the basic genetic make-up does provide the natural framework for the development of the future personal identity of the human being. Along with other determinants of our physical existence, the individual genome prescribes the biological scope of moral freedom, which on the basis of the psychosomatic unity of the person is the antechamber to the idea of human dignity and because of the elementary possibility of the responsible planning of life must be included among the areas which need protection.

The right to the chance origin of one's own existence from a natural process of procretaion in which two biological parents are involved, which is called for in the documents of the church's magisterium, therefore does not follow from a particular dignity of the process of procreation which already in itself has moral dignity and inviolability. The right of the human person to be produced by his or her own parents in a natural way is grounded, rather, in the fact that only the chance combination of two haploid nuclear cells to form a new individual human genome provides protection against becoming the object of genetic manipulation and heteronomous determination by an outside party. The objection that the biological parents also determine the genetic identity of their parents misses the decisive point, as in the process of procreation these are acting as natural beings who have no deliberate influence on the composition of the genetic identity of their children. Nor is the reference to the occurrence of monozygotic twin births in nature a tenable objection to the argument which has been put forward. Unlike human clones, twins are not identical in the sense that all their hereditary information was determined by a single alien individual. Certainly they have a common genetic heritage, but this does not derive from a single genetic copying instrument but from two biological parents who because of the chance nature of the process of procreation can never again produce a genome of precisely the same nature. Moreover the process of cloning can be repeated endlessly, so that in this way any number of identical examples of the original genome could be produced, and that does not happen in nature.

Above all, however, monozygotic twins differ from clone and donor by virtue of the contemporaneousness of their existence. They come into existence together, and both have their future ahead of them independent of each other, whereas clones would always be dictated to by expectations and predictions which have already been played out in the displaced lifetime of their predecessors. Here we must remember with Hans Jonas that human beings can be really free only if they do not know their future and their own fate, whereas clones which are displaced in time and succeed one another, to such a degree that in a hypothetical thought-experiment we could put ourselves in the situation of such beings, would be condemned to a monstrous existence without any natural quality and spontaneity.

Translated by John Bowden

Feminist Theologies and the New Genetics

Maura A. Ryan

More than half of all pregnant women in the United States this year will undergo some kind of genetic testing. Through pre-natal diagnosis, it is now possible to detect as many as 200 genetic disorders. With the success of efforts currently under way to map and sequence the human genome, experts predict that in the near future virtually all single gene conditions will be diagnosable before birth. In addition, it may soon be possible to offer inexpensive routine DNA testing for disease and disease suscepti-bility genes for a wide range of common adult onset problems, e.g., heart disease, cancer, diabetes and mental illness. One American scientist boasts: 'In fifteen years, we will probably be able to apply a single multiplex test to foetuses *in utero*, babies at birth, or in many cases, parental carriers, a test that will detect somewhere betwen 100 and 1,000 of the most common genetic diseases, genetic predispositions, and genetic risk factors . . .'[1]

The genetic revolution has profound implications for reproductive decision-making and, beyond that, for our understandings of disease and disability, conceptions of health and illness and social definitions of 'normality' and 'abnormality', as well as our decisions regarding the allocation of medical and social resources. It is not surprising that feminists have paid close attention to the growth of genetic technologies. Wary of the promises of medical 'progress' given the ambiguous, often painful, history of medical intervention in women's lives, some have joined the Feminist International Network of Resistance to Reproductive and Genetic Engineering (Finrrage). Even feminists who do not oppose developments in pre-natal diagnosis and genetic engineering tend to be cautious in their appraisal, aware of what 'unlocking the genetic code' could mean for the prevention and treatment of genetic disease, but also what it could mean for the future of reproductive choice, personal identity and social relations.

This article explores the contribution of feminist theology to ethical reflection on the new genetics. I am concerned with two sets of questions. What are the implications of expansions in genetic science and medicine for the lives of women? That is, what are the ethical issues raised by developments in genetic technology? And what contribution can a *theological* perspective make to our efforts to formulate responsible policies and practices for the use of genetic knowledge?

I

As a discipline, feminist theology has developed with a self-conscious attention to *context*, to the importance of the lived experience of persons and groups as sources for theological and ethical reflection. We should not expect, therefore, to find a single, uniform feminist theological answer to the questions posed by advances in genetic technology. Rather, as new developments generate new (or revisit old) questions, we can expect to hear a rich and varied feminist voice, as feminists speak through the particular realities of nation, race, economic status and sexual orientation. At the same time, feminist theologies are defined by a focal commitment to the well-being of women (as well as men) and a critique of long-standing patterns of gender discrimination.[2] Thus, whatever differences emerge, feminist theological analyses will share a central concern for the implications of genetic technologies for women's lives and for women's collective efforts to guarantee full and equal participation in social, political and economic life.

The first fruits of co-ordinated efforts to map and sequence the human genome are in the identification of disease-related genes, i.e., the diagnosis of genetic susceptibility and genetic disease. Even the most enthusiastic proponents of the Human Genome Project (a multi-million dollar gene-mapping and sequencing initiative) acknowledge that the therapeutic benefits of current genetic discoveries are years, maybe decades, away.[3] Thus, one important set of ethical questions concerns how we are to deal with information about genetic diseases or disease susceptibility for which treatment does not yet exist. How are we to weigh the importance of providing access to diagnostic testing, e.g., for Huntington's Disease, against the associated psychological, social and economic risks to individuals?

In countries which lack guaranteed access to health care (such as the United States), even a diagnosis of susceptibility for genetic disease could prove dangerous if used as a basis for exclusion from employment or health insurance coverage. In addition, there exist everywhere risks of social stigma attached to genetic disorders. Thus, an immediate concern in any ethical analysis of genetic technology is for the protection of every patient's right to determine whether or not she will seek genetic testing, free of coercion or the threat of genetic discrimination. We can expect feminists to join others in insisting on informed consent for genetic testing and appropriate regulation governing access to and use of genetic information by third parties.

Because the ability to identify genetic disease and disease susceptibility far outpaces the development of effective interventions, 'preventing genetic disease' in most cases means aborting affected foetuses identified through pre-natal testing (or, less often, selecting out unaffected embryos for transfer in assisted reproduction). Of obvious concern for feminist ethics are the conditions under which reproductive decisions on the basis of genetic information are likely to be made. Genetic testing is a powerful tool for reinforcing and acting on the eugenic preferences of a society (racial, sexual, physical and economic). Against the unhappy history of eugenic sterilization programmes and coerced abortion for population control or sex-selection, feminists (along with others) have insisted on the importance of protection for bodily integrity and reproductive liberty in policies governing the acquisition and use of genetic information. The current bias towards non-directiveness in genetic counselling is compatible with feminist commitments to honouring women's moral agency: those who bear the costs, feminists agree, must assess the meaning of genetic information for themselves, must choose freely whether or not they will reproduce or bring an affected foetus to term.

But, protecting the values of autonomy and bodily integrity in the 'age of the genome' requires more than simply opposing policies and practices that explicitly violate reproductive liberty in the service of social, political or economic goals. It also requires attention to conditions that create forced choices. For example, in the United States (and elsewhere), 'we live with an unspoken and unexamined-examined healthism and able-ism that puts the differences arising from disability beyond the pale'.[4] To the extent that 'healthism' or 'able-ism' means a generalized lack of commitment to meeting the physical and social needs of the disabled or overcoming obstacles to access and participation, the decision whether or not to bear a child who will be disabled cannot be a *free* choice. Where societal pressure or inadequate social and economic support render any decision to continue a pregnancy in the face of a negative diagnosis 'irresponsible', the opportunity afforded by pre-natal genetic testing quickly becomes a burden to terminate. Thus, it is important not only to question the procedures for insuring voluntariness and informed consent but to examine the subtle and complex social mechanisms by which we as societies decide which imperfections or disabilities we will tolerate and which we will not, in other words, 'who should and who should not inhabit the world'.[5]

One of the dangers in our growing reliance on genetic information in the definition and treatment of disease is the power of genetics to 'redefine socially derived syndromes as problems of the individual', shifting blame for disease, disfunction or failures to adapt from social conditions to 'inborn vulnerabilities'.[6] Pre-natal testing is valuable in reducing the incidence of birth defects and childhood disease, but increasing emphasis on genetic testing draws our attention from much more important and correctable factors; poverty, poor nutrition, inadequate access to pre-natal care and maternal age. Identifying genetically-based vulnerabilities to the effects of environmental toxins gives workers important health information, but it also allows employers merely to exclude potentially vulnerable workers rather than take responsibility for the environmental fall-out of production. Locating the genetic basis for mental illness serves responsible reproductive decision-making, but it also obscures the 'sick-making' features of contemporary social and familial life.

A related danger is the power of the genetic world-view to reduce intricate human phenomena to 'biological disorders'. The search for the 'gay gene', or genes for aggression, personal success, altruism or emotional resiliency, reveals the temptation to give a biological account of characteristics, behaviours or personal attributes which can only be understood fully within the complexity of social relationships. In the case of sexual orientation, the risk is of giving a scientific rationale to tendencies to view human sexuality narrowly through categories of 'normal' and 'abnormal'.

In general, feminists have been concerned, not only with the problem of gender discrimination, but with social patterns of inclusion and exclusion, and forms of social organization that maintain positions of privilege for some at the expense of others. As the ability to locate genetic markers for human characteristics or behaviours grows more sophisticated – or as scientists develop the ability to manipulate genetic make-up – we can expect feminist theologians, therefore, to look critically at how genetic knowledge *as social power* is likely to be used within specific societies: What cultural norms will be reinforced? What economic or political purposes served? Which goals of health and well-being will be furthered and which sidetracked? Whose health or well-being will be at stake?

Much of what I have said here pertains to the most immediate implications of advances in genetic technologies for women: increasing use of pre-natal genetic testing and the rapid development of predictive testing for genetic disease or disease susceptibility. The ethical questions posed by the new possibilities for genetic engineering are, of course, enormously important. As germ line interventions become possible, profound questions are raised about our obligations to future generations, the relationship of scientific power to created nature, and the boundaries of 'proportionate risk' in the face of genetic uncertainty. As feminists meet them within their own histories and circumstances, they are certain to remain concerned for the protection of reproductive liberty and for justice in the development and clinical application of genetic technologies, as well as to insist on a realistic assessment of the contribution of genetic technologies to human well-being.

II

As James Walter argues, moral judgments about genetic interventions involve theological presuppositions, e.g., about the nature of creation and divine providence, eschatology, the boundaries of free will and the meaning of the 'normatively human'.[7] In order to give an adequate feminist theological analysis of contemporary genetic technologies, we would have to do justice to the rich, diverse and still emerging feminist literature on this broad set of foundational questions. Given the limits of this article, however, I will simply identify three areas in which I believe feminist theological perspectives can make an important contribution to ethical reflection on the new genetics: reasoning in terms of the common good; reframing the moral significance of embodiment; and developing an ethic of stewardship.

1. The common good

Earlier, I pointed to two dangers in the growing use of genetic testing: the temptation to view disease or disability as a matter of 'individual vulnerabilities' and the temptation to use genetic information to reinforce exclusionary standards of 'normality' and 'abnormality'. Feminist commitments to an ideal of inclusive community provide an important corrective. Respect for individuality and the right to self-determination have been foundational concerns for feminist ethics. But, because feminists also value *sociality* or *relationality* as essential dimensions of moral experience, they have been critical of social models that presuppose a view of the person as fundamentally detached and self-interested or that pit individual needs against collective interests. For feminists, the work of guaranteeing the basic human rights or well-being of individuals cannot be separated from the work of creating and maintaining a just and humane social order.

The problem of disease or disability or difference for feminist theology is not, therefore, 'How do we protect the community from the diseased or disabled or different?', but, 'How do we organize our common life to make possible an equitable and dignified level of participation for every member, especially the most marginalized or the most vulnerable?' Genetic technologies can be powerful tools for addressing human suffering. But, if in the course of attempting to eliminate genetic disease we give blessing to a 'survival of the fittest' or a 'genetic perfection' social ethic, we will have bought advancements in health at a great human cost. Protecting the rights of individuals and couples in genetic testing and discerning how to direct genetic technologies for human health and well-being are urgent concerns, but the deeper concern is this. How are we to use genetic knowledge for the *common good*? What role can and will genetic technologies play in the creation of social conditions (global as well as local) in which the 'concrete, embodied needs that all persons have – for dignity, food, shelter, health, bodily integrity, non-alienating labour and cultural creativity' can be met?[8]

A continuing challenge for feminist ethics will be to develop a language of genetic responsibility alongside that of genetic rights. Genetic knowledge is inescapably *social*. Its 'truths' are about families as well as individuals. Choices based on genetic information have implications for further generations, for societies as well as individuals. We need not undermine the importance of reproductive liberty or the value of scientific progress in calling for personal and social accountability in the development and use of genetic technologies. Indeed, from the perspective of the common good, rights and liberties – as claims on the conditions all persons require for human flourishing – are intrinsically related to responsibilities.

2. Embodiment

Feminism has long been preoccupied with the problem of the body. Rejecting traditional claims about women's 'natural vocation to motherhood' or her 'inborn irrationality', feminists insisted that anatomy is *not* destiny. The body can and at times must be transcended through rational choice.[9] At the same time, they urged women to celebrate bodiliness, to 'take back their bodies' from all that threatened to diminish or devalue them. As Margaret Farley notes, feminist philosophers and theologians have sought to describe 'what it means to *be* a body as well as *have* a body', to understand one's own body as a way of 'being inserted into the world, as structured centre of activity, as body-subject, not just body object'.[10]

A growing faith in genetics confronts us with a new version of 'anatomy is destiny'. 'It's all in our genes', we are led to believe; unlocking the code is nothing less than taking charge of our fate, answering the ultimate mysteries of life and death, deliverance and doom. But feminist caution about making the body either *everything* or *nothing* is instructive here. To overestimate the genetic is to reduce the complexity of human behaviours and biological phenomena to a single factor; to underestimate the genetic is to posit a new dualism, as though the limits and frailties of bodiliness could be somehow denied. Rather, genuinely 'taking hold of our fate' means learning how to understand ourselves, whatever our particular genetic endowment, as 'inserted in the world', as 'body-subjects', living with a set of biological givens along with opportunities for rational action on our own behalf and for the sake of others.

As genetic technologies multiply, it will be important for feminist theologians to join others in probing the moral significance of embodiment. Does 'bodiliness' impose natural moral limits on what we may do in the alleviation of genetic disease or the enhancement of human personality? Is there a point at which women (as well as men) ought to be encouraged to 'take back their bodies' from the hands of genetic medicine? Most important, how do we draw the line between those genetic vulnerabilities that justice or compassion demands we alter if we can, and the shared, inescapable realities of human finitude that we must finally accept? Feminist theologians have hardly settled these questions in their long reflection on reproductive technologies. Still, there is wisdom to be drawn from their efforts to think about the problems of suffering and medicine's role, the high human costs of medical intervention in life processes, and the ambiguity of scientific promises in the context of assisted reproduction.

3. *Towards an ethic of stewardship*

The complex ethical questions posed by developments in genetics converge in this: what is a right use, a fitting use of genetic power?

The relationship of technology to nature is often portrayed by theologians as a problem of 'dominion' versus 'reverence' or 'obedience'. Worries about genetic manipulation are expressed in admonitions not to 'play God'. But feminists have found neither the language of 'dominion' nor that of a simple 'reverence' adequate for describing the contours of human freedom *vis-à-vis* creation. To assume that human beings have a right and responsibility to subdue the earth, to bring creation (including themselves) under rational control, denies the radical interdependence of all things and the reality of human creatureliness. To suppose that God's intentions for creation are coextensive with biological facts and physical laws (which ought simply to be heeded), ignores the gift of human reason and the continuing obligations of *co*-creation.

Rather, feminists have preferred the language of *stewardship* to capture the meaning of right relation in the context of scientific and medical progress. Good stewardship involves appreciation for the intrinsic value of all things, action on behalf of persons and their environment as interconnected and interdependent, and attention to the unintended as well as the intended consequences of our choices.

A full ethic of stewardship for genetic technologies has yet to be developed. But we can expect such an ethic to incorporate, e.g., a provisional openness to the use of genetic intervention to address human suffering, set within commitments to equality and mutuality in the pursuit of human well-being; respect for the concrete reality of persons as both self-determining and intrinsically relational in defining the limits of genetic manipulation; commitment to the integrity of the physical environment in the pursuit of human goals; and a vigilant attention to the temptations either of arrogance (to use genetic technologies to exploit persons or groups) or of indifference (to fail to use scientific knowledge for the benefit of those in need).

III

I have given here only the barest hint of the contribution of feminist theologies to ethical reflection on the new genetics. But it should be possible, nonetheless, to see what is important in a feminist moral vision and thus what feminist theologians can offer in the difficult questions we face. Rooted in the lived struggle for equality, feminist ethics brings us back continually to the question: how will genetic technologies affect the lives of individual women and men, particularly the most marginalized? Yet, committed to social transformation, feminist ethics presses us always beyond the individual to what is finally at stake: how will genetic technologies serve the creation of a world in which the claims of all to dignity, food, shelter, health care and meaningful social interaction are honoured?

Notes

1. Charles Cantor, 'The Challenges to Technology and Informatics', in *The Code of Codes*, edited by Donald Kevies and Leroy Hood, Cambridge, Mass. 1992, 98–111.

2. See Margaret A. Farley, 'Feminist Theology and Bioethics', in *Women's Consciousness. Women's Conscience*, ed. Barbara Hilkert Andolsen, Christine E. Gudorf and Mary D. Pellauer, Minneapolis 1985, 288.

3. See *The Code of Codes* (n. 1), 296.

4. Ibid., 234.

5. Ruth Hubbard, 'Eugenics: New Tools, Old Ideas', in *Embryos, Ethics and Women's Rights*, ed. Elaine Hoffman Baruch et al., New York 1988, 231.

6. Dorothy Nelkin, 'The Social Power of Genetic Information', in *The Code of Codes* (n. 1), 183.

7. James J. Walter, 'Presuppositions to Moral Judgment on Human Genetic Manipulation', *Chicago Studies*, November 1994, 228–39.

8. Beverly Wildung Harrison, 'Theological Reflection in the Struggle for Liberation', in *Making the Connections*, ed. Carol S. Robb, Boston 1985, 254.

9. Farley, 'Feminist Theology and Bioethics' (n. 2), 292.

10. Ibid., 293.

Cloning: Technical Reality and Ethical Evaluation

Marciano Vidal

At the end of February the review *Nature* (27 February 1997, no. 385,pp. 810–13) carried the news of a scientific breakthrough made by Dr Ian Willmut and his colleagues at the Roslin Institute of Edinburgh: the cloning of a sheep from a differentiated cell. The fact that this cloning had been done with a higher mammal and, above all, from an adult or differentiated cell, gave this scientific achievement a special significance not only in public opinion but also among the scientific community. The possibility of cloning human beings was brought ever closer. The division of human embryos (cloning of embryonic omnipotential cells) had been achieved in 1993, but now the possibility of cloning human beings by means of differentiated cells took on a new impetus. One newspaper expressed this possibility under a somewhat alarmist headline: 'Today, the sheep; tomorrow, the shepherd.'

In the following pages I set out to analyse the ethical dimension of cloning, in its general sense, though with particular attention to human cloning. This will be done in fairly summary form, as required by the context of an article in *Concilium*. Although I take the detailed scientific and technical data as given, I start by citing some examples to describe the reality of cloning. I follow this with an overview of the approaches needed to reach an ethical evaluation. These two sections correspond to the two aspects stated in the title: an analysis of cloning as a *technical reality* and in its *ethical dimension*.

I. The reality of cloning

1. The term and the reality
The term 'clone' comes from the Greek and means 'branch' or 'cutting'.

It is used in biology to refer to organisms originated from others not by sexual reproduction but through division or splitting. Sexual reproduction supposes, in biology, an enrichment and a variation; it produces a being with the double (diploid) genetic coding that comes from the genetic half (haploid) of each of its germinal cells.

Cloning is the process through which identical organisms are reproduced; that is, with the same genetic coding (the same DNA) as the organisms that preceded them. Reproduction through division exists in nature, and there is, therefore, production of genetically identical organisms: this is reproduction by *parthenogenesis* (virginal) or by *autogenesis* (self-creating). The cloning examined here, however, is not what might be described as 'natural', but that brought about through a special human intervention.

It is worth noting that the cloned being is 'identical' to its predecessor only in its genetic make-up, not in its overall reality. It is identical in the genotype but not in the phenotype, that is, in everything that comes from the environment (beginning with gestation processes and ending in cultural influence), from formation, from freedom, and from the other influences that make up the identity of an individual. In this appreciation I am referring to a possible human cloning. So we have to remove the cloning of geniuses or saints from our imagination. It is no more possible to replicate a St John of the Cross from genetic material than it is to reduce a Johann Sebastian Bach to his clonable biological make-up. In fact, cloned beings are less identical than monocygotic or univiteline twins.

2. *Organisms susceptible to cloning*

Cloning, as a special human intervention in the reproduction process, can be carried out in all realms of nature: in micro-organisms, in the vegetable and animal kingdoms, and in the human species.

The manipulation of micro-organisms (viruses and bacteria) for biotechnical purposes involves the phenomenon of cloning. So, for example, it is cloning to introduce human genes into bacteria so that these human genes will replicate themselves and so produce organic material, such as human insulin, human interferon, the growth hormone, and so on. The same basis of replication is used to produce viruses and bacteria for other purposes: to dissolve oil slicks, to eliminate plagues, to produce nitrogenous fertilizers, and even to manufacture biological weapons. These forms of reproducing micro-organisms, although they suppose the fact of producing identical copies, are not considered to fall within the ethical parameters of cloning properly so-called.

The same should be said of many interventions in the genetics of the vegetable kingdom. Replication in vegetable species is a habitual practice. It is done in an unsophisticated way when an agricultural worker grafts fruit trees: the graft is nothing other than a part of a previous organism (another fruit tree), which replicates itself in the wild tree converted, through the graft, into a fruit tree. On a higher technical level, cloning in vegetative species is carried out by genetic modifications (transgenic plants), replicating genetically modified species (of potatoes, tomatoes, maize, wheat, rice, soya, etc.). The aim of this process is to increase agricultural yield, both quantitatively and qualitatively.

Cloning becomes a more significant phenomenon when it is carried out on animal species. Advances in cellular and molecular biology have, in our century, brought about embryonic excision (the artificial production of twins) in the 1930s; the cloning of amphibians (toads) through differentiated cells in the 1960s; the cloning of mice, using embryonic cells, in the 1980s, followed by the cloning of mice, sheep and monkeys, all still using embryonic cells. As I said, the cloning of the sheep Dolly in 1997, from a differentiated cell, marked a highly significant scientific and technical leap forward. Until then, no one had succeeded in cloning mammals using somatic (adult) cells.

From the scientific point of view, the possibility of cloning in the human species cannot be ruled out. In 1993 the division of human embryos was achieved in George Washington University in the USA. At present there is no objective and trustworthy evidence that human cloning from differentiated cells has taken place. This would seem to be the ultimate in cloning and the operation that raises the most acute ethical questions.

3. Techniques used (or usable) for cloning in animal species (and in the human species)

There are two basic procedures. The first is carried out at the embryo stage before implantation in the womb. In the phases following fertilization cells are omnipotential, meaning that they all have the capacity to generate a new being. If the embryo is divided at this stage (two to eight cells), several genetically identical beings are produced. Monocygotic twins originate naturally at this stage. When special human intervention is involved, cloning by excision or twin fission takes place. This technique normally presupposes *in vitro* fertilization.

The second process consists of reprogramming the nucleus of a differentiated (adult, or somatic) cell through transferring it to a previously enucleated ovum. This is usually done in three stages. First, a somatic cell is obtained from the organism to be reproduced or cloned.

Second, the nucleus of this somatic cell is transferred to an ovum obtained from a different individual and earlier 'denuclearized'; the new germinal cell contains the genetic coding of the first individual. Then, the fertilized ovum is placed in the uterus of another individual, which is the one that will gestate it.

This second process was followed in the case of Dolly the sheep. The somatic cell obtained was a mammary cell (from the udder). 277 fusions with as many other denuclearized ova were made; this number of fusions produced only twenty-nine viable embryos, thirteen of which were implanted in the uterus, only one of which reached its final goal. The team that developed the technique accepted the production of chimeras and monsters before bringing the experiment to a successful conclusion.

The first process – division of a pre-implanted embryo – has been carried out in species close to the human. Scientists in Oregon have succeeded in producing two monkeys from cloned embryos. As already noted, the division of human embryos during the pre-implant stage has also been achieved, without proceeding to further development (1993).

It is worth stressing that the second process, cloning from differentiated cells, is of greater interest, since it is the technique that achieves the ultimate aims of cloning: knowing the individual to be replicated, obtaining the closest possible identification with it, and having the possibility of replicating the same copy a large number of times. This has led some scientists to seek to reserve the term and concept 'cloning' for this process, calling the first 'twin excision or fission'. For the time being, I shall refer to cloning by both methods in this study.

4. Advantages and risks

The benefits cloning can bring are evident. The first, undoubtedly, is that to science. Fundamental investigation is one of the defining activities of human beings. A world of research is being created around cloning, in which one of the great human interests, the acquisition of scientific knowledge, is being pursued.

Cloning is also beneficial as applied research. In the vegetable kingdom it can bring notable advantages in increasing and improving agricultural resources; it can also serve to protect species in danger of extinction. The same is true in the animal kingdom, where animals that are real 'super-producers' of, for example, wool or milk, can be reproduced. Animal cloning can bring the following direct benefits to humans: 1. production of and research into new medicines; 2. research into genetic diseases, such as cancer; 3. supply of organs and tissues for transplants ('xeno-transplants'). In biotechnology it has raised considerable hopes of obtaining pharmacological products derived from living beings. In fact, a pharmaceutics firm financially supported the Dolly project, with consequent benefits accruing to it: the value of its shares rose by 65% as a result of the successful outcome of the experiment.

The cloning of human beings would bring the benefit of making tissues available for use in transplants; the production of identical human beings would also increase the success rate of transplants. There is already talk of 'clonal medicine', to emphasize the therapeutic benefits that cloning of human beings would afford.

Leaving human cloning aside for the moment, the risks this practice implies in the vegetable kingdom and, particularly, in the animal, can be classed into the following groups:

— it can lead to breakdown of barriers between species, so provoking a biological discord in creation;

— it can work against biodiversity: by eliminating some species, homogenizing others excessively, and destroying in the present certain genes that may be convenient or even necessary in the future;

— it is not impossible that it may produce epidemics, both intra-specific and extra-specific.

Pondering the advantages and risks is not yet an ethical consideration in its strict and full sense, unless morality is to be reduced to a utilitarian play of advantages and disadvantages. This is not the ethical understanding underlying this study. And yet, ethical discernment has to take account of all the implications of the reality, among which the economy of risks and benefits has to be counted.

5. *Variations in 'human imagining'*

The reality of cloning would not be fully described without alluding to its meta-scientific implications. Cloning has become a great metaphor for reality; people talk of cloned cars, politicians, businessmen, priests . . . And not only this: the reality of cloning echoes with desires, utopias, fears and projections, all of which form part of human imagining. It seems as though cloning promises to start realizing our dreams of:

— 'autogenesis': the Faustian desire to perpetuate ourselves as we are indefinitely;

— 'virginal' procreation: procreation without sexual intervention, without 'mixing', without the impurity of 'desire': 'clean' procreation, aseptic and technical.

— the feminist revenge of procreation 'without a man';

— the total projection of the 'father' into a son identical to him – and this in a society in which the father-figure is tending to lose its importance;

– the real existence of 'doubles', of '*sosias*', of 'twins' (the Spartan Dioscuri Castor and Pollux, Dostoyevsky's *sosias*, Oscar Wilde's *Portrait of Dorian Gray*, and so on).

These repercussions of cloning in the social imagination come not only from the scientific-technical fact in itself, but also from representations of it in films such as *The Boys from Brazil* and *Jurassic Park*, and a mass of books beginning with Aldous Huxley's *Brave New World*. Ethical evaluation of cloning has to take account of these 'imaginary' implications so as, above all, to introduce rationality into them. Ethics cannot be formulated on the basis of 'furthest limits' of imagination, only on that of the limits to genuine human reasoning.

II. Approaches to ethical discernment

1. From spontaneous reaction to rational consideration

The scientific-technological advances in cloning have produced spontaneous reactions in both public opinion and the scientific community. The cloning of Dolly the sheep has been compared to the opening of Pandora's Box: many 'terrors' have come from cloning, but it remains in the realm of 'hope' – in this case, hope in the ethical nature of science.[1]

Spontaneous reaction to cloning falls under two sets of feelings:

– on the one hand, admiration for the success achieved; an increase in the 'self-esteem' felt at belonging to the human race, a self-esteem so often shaken by the existence of wars, of injustice, of intransigence; 'science' seems to form the unconquerable bastion of human pride;

– on the other hand, fear of the possible bad uses ('abuses') to which scientific knowledge can be put; in this case, the greatest fear is of the extrapolation of cloning to the human species.

Spontaneous reaction cannot just stop there: it has to lead on to rational consideration. It is at this stage of rational (not 'spontaneous') 'consideration' (and not 'reaction') that ethics intervenes as an important approach to introducing reasoning into human decision-making.

In this respect it is gratifying to observe the presence of ethical discourse in the current biological revolutions. This did not happen when comparable research and experimentation was being carried out in physics. The splitting of the atom was not accompanied by the sort of ethical reflection that is now taking place in regard to cellular fission. Bioethics is one of the most notable contributions made by the human mind in the latter part of the twentieth century.

2. An ethical paradigm for cloning

Ethical reasoning takes place within a model of discourse that I am here calling a 'paradigm'. I am opposed to two ethical paradigms that operate in a simplistic (a-dialectical) form and with a fundamentalist (totalitarian and intransigent) stamp:

– that of saying 'no' to anything that seems to imply change, transformation, variation of an order deemed 'sacral' (natural) and immutable (objective);

– that of saying 'still more' to anything in the scientific-technological field that fuels the forward rush, without thinking where it wants to go and what means it uses to get there.

I prefer an ethical paradigm of discernment, in which the following factors are conjoined: a positive attitude to everything that means progress; a realization of the ambivalence of progress – able to be put to good or bad ends; an appeal to human responsibility to direct the course of progress; the need for a general criterion that guides responsibility objectively and, consequently, gives meaning to progress. The following paragraphs deal with some of the factors in this paradigm.

Ethical discernment has to be exercised taking account of the ambivalence of all human progress. This situation is today expressed by the term 'risk society'. We live at a moment in history when we have to take technological decisions: to do so we have to evaluate their risk and, consequently, consider the options with their attendant advantages and disadvantages.[2]

Faced with this risk situation, there can be no ethical attitude other than responsibility. It was the German philosopher H. Jonas who particularly stressed the responsibility principle for ethics at the present time, above all with reference to scientific-technological advances.[3] Responsibility has to include taking subsequent generations into account: we have to make use of creation and make progress while taking account of the fact that subsequent generations also need to enjoy the benefits we do.

These two reference points – assessing risk and appealing to responsibility – lead to a third criterion of an axiological nature. Risks and responsibility have to be measured by the value of an authentic process of humanization. It is the criterion of humanization that gives meaning and direction to the decisions that need to be taken in the field of scientific and technological progress. Humanization, as defined in the encyclical *Populorum progressio*, means the realization of 'the whole person and of all persons', that is, seeking the integral good of all as one.[4]

3. Basic ethical values

In the light of the ethical paradigm outlined, the following basic values can be proposed as subject for moral discernment on cloning, distinguishing between cloning of vegetables and animals and that of human beings:

(i) Cloning of vegetables and animals

In itself, the cloning of vegetables and animals does not involve the same degree of ethical implication as attaches to the cloning of human beings. Nevertheless, we need to bear in mind that:

– interventions in vegetable and animal genetics have to be thought out and carried out with a view to the general good of humankind; accepting the normal profit from investments made in this field as in others, we must not fall into new forms of economic imperialism, in this case biotechnological imperialism;

– there are limits to biotechnological interventions when these can bring about ecological disasters – disappearance of species, new risks to other species – or risk to the human species – transmission of viruses or uncontrollable pollution.

(ii) Cloning of human beings

Any intent to build a better humanity is worthy of praise; we cannot on principle condemn the desire to bring about an improvement in the human species, even in such an important field as genetics. Nevertheless, we should bear in mind that there are limits to this desire for improvement or variation, limits that are at the same time positive indicators for a better direction of progress.

As things stand at present, the cloning of human beings has many counter-indications. Some of the main ones are:

– human beings have the dignity of persons and cannot be reduced to 'objects'; the cloning process involves so many interventions, and of such a nature, that it is impossible for it not to treat human reality as an 'object';

– major 'manipulations' have first to be carried out on the cell from which the clonic nucleus is obtained, which can give rise to serious 'malformations' that can be transmitted to the new being: as already noted, those responsible for the cloning of Dolly accepted the production of chimeras and of monsters before obtaining the desired result.

– biodiversity is an ethical criterion that also has to be taken account of in the human species;

– the most important consideration of all is that human beings have their own identity; cloning impacts directly on this basic requirement for being a person.

These ethical reasons for invalidating the viability of human cloning should not clip the wings of human mental endeavour. This should continue to raise serious philosophical questions concerning the meaning of human evolution.

Is the right to 'chance', to genetic 'diversity', to personal 'difference' something basic to human evolution? Should such rights be tempered with the affirmation of 'freedom of choice', with the necessary affirmation of 'otherness' in the principle of individuation? If manipulations of vegetable and animal species were needed for the human 'take-off' from Neolithic man, why not accept other new 'manipulations' for the take-off into the new age some people envisage, which they call the Neogenic? These and other questions have to remain open, even though for the time being ethical reasoning has to regard the cloning of human beings as morally unviable.

4. Towards a universally shared ethical consensus

There are ethical values that should have a universally shared expression. I believe one of these to be the genetic identity of each person. There are positive signs of a universally shared tendency to drop human cloning from human prospects. Suffice it to record the standpoints adopted by the major ethical authorities of present-day humankind:

– The Vatican is opposed to 'obtaining a human being with no connection to sexuality by means of "twin fission", cloning, parthenogenesis' on the grounds that this would contradict 'the dignity of both human procreation and the conjugal union';[5] furthermore, it has asked all nations to pass a law prohibiting human cloning.

– The OMS has issued a declaration against cloning (18 March 1997).[6] UNESCO has also declared the same understanding, further working on a proposal to declare the human genome the patrimony of all humankind.[7]

– The European Parliament has approved a resolution opposed to human cloning (12 March 1997).[8]

– National Commissions for Bioethics in several countries, as well as various political authorities, have declared themselves against human cloning. Among those who have taken this stand is the American President Bill Clinton.[9]

This ethical consensus is beginning to be translated into the legal field. In the German law on Embryo Protection (1991) cloning is expressly forbidden (art. 6). The 1995 Spanish Penal Code declares 'the creation of identical human beings by cloning or other procedures directed toward racial selection' punishable (by one to five years in prison and six to ten years of special restrictions; art. 161.2).

We have, however, to place our trust in an ethical understanding reached in conscience by the whole of humanity rather than in laws and punishments. We need to raise consciousness of the responsibility that has to go alongside scientific and technical progress. Science has to be accompanied by con-science if we want the human adventure to proceed towards ever higher quotas of humanization for all, and especially for less favoured individuals and groups.

Translated by Paul Burns

Notes

1. J.-R. Lacadena, 'Cloning: a New Pandora's Box?' in *Crítica* no. 844, 1997, 7.
2. G. Bechman (ed.), *Risiko und Gesellschaft. Grundlagen und Ergebnisse interdisziplinären Risikoforschung*, Opladen 1993.
3. H. Jonas, *The Imperative of Responsibility*, Chicago 1984.
4. *Populorum progressio* (1967), n. 14.
5. *Donum vitae* (1987), I, 6.
6. Text in *Medicina e Morale* 47, 1997, 323–5.
7. Cf N. Lenoir, 'UNESCO, Genetics and Human Rights', *Kennedy Institute of Ethics Journal* 7, 1997, 31–42.
8. Text in *Medicina e Morale* 47, 1997, 323–7.
9. B. Clinton, 'Human values and cloning', 22 June 1997.

Bibliographical Note
(to 30 June 1997)

It is noteworthy that the *Encyclopedia of Bioethics*, in five volumes, revised edition 1995 (ed. W. T. Reich), has no monographic article on cloning.

Pioneering studies on the ethics of cloning (and on genetic engineering in general) have to include:

P. Ramsey, *Fabricated Man. The Ethics of Genetic Control*, Newhaven 1970.

H. Jonas, *Technik, Medezin, Ethik*, Frankfurt 1985, 162–203.

Recent studies from the standpoint of theological ethics:

M. F. dos Anjos, 'Etica e clonagem humana na questão dos paradigmas', in *REB* 55, 1995, 105–17.

A. Fiori and E. Sgreccia, 'La clonazione', *Medicina e Morale* 47, 1997, 229–39.

J. Gafo, 'La sorpresa científica de la clonación,' *Razón y Fe* 235, 1997, 363–76.

E. García Peregrín, 'La clonación a distintos niveles: un problema científico y ético', *Proyección* 42, 1994, 123–34.

J.-R. Lacadena, 'La clonación: aspectos científicos y éticos,' *Anales de la Real Academia de Farmacia* 63, 1997, 273–93.

J. Reiter, 'Klonen von Tieren und Menschen. Bioethik auf der Suche nach ethischen Grenzen', *Stimmen der Zeit* 215, 1997, 363–73.

G. Russo, 'La clonazione di soggetti umani. Riflessioni bioetiche, norma sociali e giuridiche,' *Itinerarium* 4, 1996, 153–80; 5, 1997, 125–51.

The Ethics of Medical Genetics
An Annotated Bibliography

Sigrid Graumann and Christof Mandry

The Human Genome Project

The Human Genome Project (HGP) and its aims are very important for the present state of genetic research and future developments. In his historical study Cook-Degan (1994) describes the scientific politics behind the HGP, including the aims with which concomitant ethical and social research was initiated. As a result of sensitivity to the experiences with eugenics in the USA and in Europe at the beginning of this century, from the beginning the public and some politicians feared that the deciphering of the human genome could be associated with eugenic aims. There is considerable argument as to whether this is in fact the case. Schulz (1991) and Kevles (1995) each examine present research and medical applications in the light of the history of eugenics. In the context of present-day democratic research institutions Kevles can establish no tendency towards eugenics; in her feminist investigation Schulz comes to the opposite conclusion. The collection edited by Shiva and Moser (1995) can serve as background reading for the feminist view of biotechnology and biomedicine. The differences in assessing whether the HGP has any connection with eugenic tendencies essentially derive from different understandings of the term 'eugenics' (see Paul in Weir, Lawrence and Fales 1994). The majority of medical and bioethical works use a narrower concept of eugenics, in the sense of political projects to improve the human heritage; works with a sociological orientation and those which are critical of culture are usually based on a more complex understanding of eugenics, in the sense of a change of values as a result of changed social practice.

Genetic research on human beings and medical practice

Various studies assessing the consequence of techniques provide information about the present state of the application of genetic diagnosis or the public discussion on gene therapy; the critical ethical points also already become clear in these (Hennen, Petermann and Schmitt 1996; Österreichische Akademie der Wissenschaften 1996; Petermann, Hennen and Schmitt 1994; Bayertz, Schmidtke and Schreiber 1995; De Wachter 1993). The genuinely ethical problems of research into the genome are reflected in a considerable number of composite volumes. These always also consider the applications of genetic knowledge in prenatal or pre-symptomatic postnatal diagnosis, in screening programmes, possible use of information by employers or insurance companies and in the forensic sphere (the so-called genetic fingerprint) (Ellermann and Opolka 1991; Beckmann, Istel, Leipoldt and Reichert 1991; Sass 1991; Haker, Hearn and Steigleder 1993; Frey 1995). American studies pay special attention to ethical legal questions which arise as the HGP progresses (Rothstein 1991); the consequences for the fair treatment of individual genetic risks in private and public health welfare systems are also a matter of controversy (Murphy and Lappé 1994).

The Italian national bioethics committee has worked out a statement on the ethical assessment of the HGP (Comitato Nazionale per la Bioetica 1994). This paper, which is clearly stamped by the scientist's standpoint, comes to the conclusion that genetic research does not raise any new kinds of problems and is therefore to be seen and assessed within the framework of the usual ethics of research. By contrast, the more journalistic collection of articles by Wess (1995), which also includes statements from the churches, offers a good introduction to typical positions critical of genome research and gene technology.

Gene diagnosis and genetic counselling

Compared with other fields of application, at present genetic methods are being most widely used in the medical diagnosis of embryos and premature births and in establishing whether genetic defects or dispositions are being handed on in particular family situations. Both the practitioners of human genetic counselling and ethicists often refer to acceleration of the extension of genetic prenatal diagnosis brought about by the growth of genetic knowledge, the pressure of expectations and the widespread anxieties among the population, and finally by the developments in laws relating to the responsibilities of doctors. As a result of this, genetic counselling over pregnancy is increasingly becoming the rule and prenatal screening has *de facto* become socially established, although there are no real screening programmes (Hennen, Petermann and Schmitt 1996; Wolff in Schöne-Seifert and Krüger 1991; Mieth and Haker in Brandt 1997). At the same time a divide is increasingly opening up between the mass of investigations and the quality and availability of qualified advice in cases of conflict. In general, the institution of genetic counselling, the aims it pursues and its theory, are at the centre of the ethical evaluation of genetic diagnosis. Well thought-out genetic counselling today is usually non-directive, and the theory and practice of this character are discussed from various perspectives (Ratz 1995). How are the autonomy of those seeking advice and the knowledge of one's own genetic make-up to be assessed? Does knowledge really heighten the individual's possibility of action and thus lead to an increase in autonomy, as some philosophers seem to think (e.g. in Schöne-Seifert and Krüger 1991)? Be this as it may, too little attention is paid to the fact that the mere pressure of the responsibility which medical counsellors have in many states is leading to a degree of directedness in counselling which is tending to make its mark on prenatal diagnosis.

In general there is more than just feminist resistance to the subtle genetic control of procreation and selection by criteria which are formulated genetically but defined socially (Basen, Eichler and Lippmann 1993; from the perspective of the handicapped and their relatives, Neuer-Milbach and Tarneden 1994). Here feminist theoreticians also emphasize the connection with international population control by the medicalization of procreation (Wichterich 1994). Ethicists see the focal points of this complex of problems, which is far from having been discussed completely, in questions about the protection of the life of embryos, the implicit assessment of the quality of 'impaired life', the right of those who seek counsel to self-determination and the conflict between the rapid growth in knowledge and the possibilities for action which do not keep up with it, along with the social changes which are brought about indirectly by genetics and which lead to fears of a society regulated by genetic discussion (summaries in Schöne-Seifert and Krüger in ibid., 1991; Neubeck-Fischer in Beckmann, Istel, Leipoldt and Reichert 1991 are very critical; Marteau and Richards 1996 offer a wide range of perspectives).

The question of the rights of future generations or persons who do not exist and the 'confused' moral intuitions connected with it stand at the centre of Heyd's (1992) reflections. On the basis of metaethical considerations he concludes that interests and wishes can be validated only for existing human beings as moral agents.

Gene therapy

In the ethical debate over gene therapy, which is still in its beginnings, distinctions have been established on the one hand between somatic gene therapy and germ line gene therapy and on the other between a therapeutic and a non-therapeutic aim (enhancement and eugenics). On the basis of this twofold differentiation it is often argued that somatic gene therapy is analogous to organ and tissue transplants and therefore in principle permissible (Walters and Palmer 1997). It is to be assessed in the same way as other experimental therapies, i.e. it is to be applied and developed in certain conditions, taking account of the potential risks in clinical experiments (Rehmann-Sutter and Müller 1995; Bayertz, Schmidtke and Schreiber 1995). So far there have been reservations about the clinical success of somatic gene therapy, though there has nevertheless been optimism about its potential (cf. the report of the US National Institute of Health: Orkin and Motulsky 1995; Bayertz, Schmidtke and Schreiber 1995). With few exceptions, in particular the question of risk, which is central to the wider discussion of the consequences of techniques and is discussed from many perspectives, plays only a subsidiary role in the discussion of medical ethics. The report by Petermann, Hennen and Schmidt (1994) refers to three controversial opinions on the risks of somatic gene therapy and comes to the conclusion that not only does account need to be taken of the risks for patients; risks for third parties from the origination of infectious viruses following a gene transfer cannot be ruled out. However, in the formulation of criteria for the use of somatic gene therapy, the usual perspective adopted is one which is directed exclusively towards the individual well-being of the patients concerned, in accordance with the current regulation of clinical experiments and the interest of the doctor. Therefore gene therapy should be undertaken only when there are no (longer any) alternative therapies available, if an isolated gene is involved and if the method has already produced sufficiently certain results in experiments on animals (de Wachter 1993). The benefit-risk ratio in therapeutic experiment has to be compared with the alternative therapy; with the most seriously ill patients who have 'run out of' therapies, a high or even unclear risk can be taken (Schmidt in Rehmann-Sutter and Müller 1995). Furthermore, there is much argument over the individual assessments of risk based on different risk theories (cf. Rehmann-Sutter in Rehmann-Sutter and Müller 1995; Kollek in Elstner 1997).

However, there is no argument that the autonomy of patients is to be preserved through their informed consent. It is conceded that the procedures entailed by this requirement raise practical and regulatory problems (Rehmann-Sutter and Müller 1995; de Wachter 1993). There is far less discussion of the question how the preservation of the patient's autonomy can be ensured if the prognosis of chances and risks on which the patient's decision is based is communicated by a doctor who is (also) interested in research.

Most studies also go into the question of the legitimate approach to gene therapy (de Wachter 1993) and provide information about attempts at legal and constitutional regulation in Europe and the USA (Sass 1991; Bayertz, Schmidtke and Schreiber 1995). However, the question arises whether there is a need to discuss not only fair distribution in the sense of the selection of patients for a technology the availability of which is very restricted, or also more generally the issue of social justice, given the limited resources there are for medicine and science.

Far more controversial than somatic gene therapy is the assessment of germ line gene therapy. 1995 saw the high point of the discussion; since then, hardly any monographs or book-contributions have appeared on this topic. At all events, today we can no longer assume that germ line therapy is generally rejected. A small minority adduce categorical arguments. Most European voices regard only a strictly therapeutic aim as ethically legitimate; others regard arguments against eugenics or enhancement as untenable (for a critical survey of more recent ethical discussion of germ line therapy see Graumann 1997). It is striking that reflections on the use of germ line therapy often move in the speculative realm. For example, Walters and Palmer (1997) discuss the legitimacy of the genetic improvement of physical, intellectual and moral human characteristics and deduce quite abstruse scenarios of social change from this.

Social and cultural consequences of genetic research on human beings

Studies are increasingly appearing which deal with the social and cultural dimensions of human genetics. For example, there is a fear that the climate will become increasingly hostile to the handicapped as a result of the establishment of genetic techniques and the growing social expectations attached to them (Neuer-Milbach and Tarneden 1994). Croyle's (1995) composite sociological volume also investigates the effects of genetic screening on social psychology from a more comprehensive perspective. Here some scepticism is expressed about the expectation in health policy that the knowledge of persons at risk because of their disposition will cause them to take precautionary measures over their health. On the question of the feared effects of social discrimination, the loss of insurance or changed family circumstances, this volume calls for further research. An original work of social philosophy, which also contains legal and ethnological approaches (Ulanowsky 1995), is particularly concerned with changes in the understanding and functioning of the family and the attitudes and actions of relatives. The various contributions assume that the family relationship has biological (i.e. genetic), social and legal dimensions which under the conditions of liberalism and individualism no longer coincide; indeed they are possibly drifting apart even more markedly as a result of modern technologies in procreation.

In general, various problem areas are discussed under the heading 'social implications of modern human genetics'. Further developments in the law are being called for to counter eugenic developments and social discrimination or discrimination by employers and insurance companies; the popular reporting of genetic knowledge in the mass media brings its own problems, and is also to be expected to have effects on social and individual self-understanding. At the moment one can do no more than guess at the new trends that predictive genetic testing will introduce for personal life and personal identity and the old ones that it will reinforce (Marteau and Richards 1996; Weir, Lawrence and Fales 1994). Both these volumes also discuss the implicit consequences for problems of gender and race and how future generations will be involved.

Ethical discussion often takes up the way in which public discourse is stamped by the vocabulary of genetics and the influence of genetic ideas – whether these are scientifically justified or not – on widespread social models, along with the fear of the expected consequences. It is to the credit of the study by Nelkin and Lindee (1995) in the sphere of the cultural sciences that it makes an empirical investigation of these rather vague conjectures. In their evaluation of the popular culture of the USA, these authors investigate the way in which the social fascination with 'the gene' is expressed, 'the gene' increasingly being used as the explanatory model for social and individual modes of behaviour and states. Here they show how 'gene' as a biological concept and 'gene' as a construct of social significance interact: the rhetorical strategies adopted by geneticists and scientific managers in making their promises on the one hand raise social expectations and utilize them, but on the other hand have an effect on public concepts and models.

Knowledge of genetics

The ambivalence of the increase in knowledge of genetics is a central problem in ethical discussion. When is it desirable to know about one's own genetic make-up, who has a right to this knowledge, and when may one refuse this knowledge and to whom? The composite volume edited by Chadwick et al. (1997) makes an important contribution to this complex of problems. It discusses the 'right to know or not to know' in connection with the interest of third parties (members of the family, employers, insurance companies, the public), on the basis of individual data and against the background of a public health system.

Waldschmidt (1996) looks very critically at the actual significance of individuals and their rights in human genetics. Her basic thesis is that genetic counselling represents a power dispositive in Foucault's sense (for Foucault in this connection see Sawicki 1991), which controls the definition of deviation and normality.

Making social and political decisions

Finally, Elstner's (1997) distinguished and interesting volume discusses models of political participation which would make it possible to deal practically with this situation, starting from the assumption that there are conflicts of values in the dispute over the acceptance of gene technology which cannot be quickly settled. This book not only reflects on theoretical techniques and political scientific considerations but also presents concrete models and cases of the social management of dissent.

Translated by John Bowden

Bibliography

Basen, Gwynne, Eichler, Margrit and Lippmann, Abby (eds), (1993): *Misconceptions*, Quebec.

Bayertz, Kurt, Schmidtke, Jörg and Schreiber, H. J. (eds) (1995): *Somatische Gentherapie*, Stuttgart, Jena and New York.

Beckmann, Dorothee, Istel, Karin, Leipoldt, Michael and Reichert, Hansjörg (eds) (1991): *Humangenetik – Segen fur die Menschen oder unkalkulierbares Risiko?*, Frankfurt am Main, Bern and New York.

Brandt, Peter (ed.) (1997): *Zukunft der Gentechnik*, Basel, Boston and Berlin.

Chadwick, Ruth, Levitt, Mairi and Shickle, Darren (1997): *The Right to Know and the Right Not to Know*, Aldershot.

Comitato Nazionale per la Bioetica (1994): *Progetto Genoma Umano, Roma 18 marzo 1994*.

Cook-Degan, Robert (1994): *The Gene Wars. Science, Politics, and the Human Genome*, New York and London.

Croyle, Robert T. (ed.) (1995): *Psychosocial Effects of Screening for Disease Prevention and Detection*, New York and Oxford.

Ellermann, Rolf and Opolka, Uwe (eds) (1991): *Genomanalyse: Ihre biochemischen, medizinischen und politischen Aspekte*, Frankfurt am Main and New York.

Elstner, Marcus (ed.) (1997): *Gentechnik, Ethik und Gesellschaft*, Berlin, Heidelberg and New York.

Frey, Hans-Dieter (ed.) (1995): *HUGO – 5 Jahre Humangenomprojekt. Wissenschaftliche Ziele, ethische, rechtliche und soziale Aspekte (Landesbiologentag 1995)*, Tübingen.

Graumann, Sigrid (1997): 'The Debate about the Moral Evaluation of Germ Line Therapy – A Critical Overview', *Biomedical Ethics* Vol. 2, 12–16.

Haker, Hille, Hearn, Richard and Steigleder, Klaus (eds) (1993): *Ethics of Human Genome Analysis. European Perspectives*, Tübingen.

Hennen, Leonhard, Petermann, Thomas and Schmitt, Joachim J. (1996): *Genetische Diagnostik – Chancen und Risiken: der Bericht des Büros für Technikfolgen-Abschätzung zur Genomanalyse*, Berlin.

Heyd, David (1992): *Genethics. Moral Issues in the Creation of People*, Berkeley, Los Angeles and Oxford.

Kevles, Daniel J. (1995): *In the Name of Eugenics. Genetics and the Uses of Human Heredity*, fourth edition, Cambridge, Mass. and London.

Marteau, Theresa and Richards, Martin (eds) (1996): *The Troubled Helix. Social and Psychological Implications of the New Human Genetics*, Cambridge.

Murphy, Timothy F. and Lappé, Marc A. (eds) (1994): *Justice and the Human Genome Project*, Berkeley, Los Angeles and London.

Nelkin, Dorothy and Lindee, M. Susan (1995): *The DNA Mystique. The Gene as a Cultural Icon*, New York.

Neuer-Milbach, Therese and Tarneden, Rudi (eds) (1994): *Vom Recht auf Anderssein. Anfrage an pränatale Diagnostik und humangenetische Beratung*, Düsseldorf.

Österreichische Akademie der Wissenschaften (1996): *Genanlytische Untersuchungen – individuelle und gesellschaftliche Auswirkungen*, Vienna.

Orkin, Stuart H. and Motulsky, Arno G. (eds) (1995): *Report and Recommendations of the Panel to Assess the NIH Investment in Research on Gene Therapy*, National Institute of Health USA.

Petermann, Thomas, Hennen, Leonhard and Schmitt, Joachim J. (1994): *Stand und Perspektiven naturwissenschaftlicher und medizinischer Problemlösungen bei der Entwicklung gentherapeutischer Heilmethoden, Projekt 'Monitoring Gentherapie' des Büros für Technikfolgenabschätzung beim Deutschen Bundestag*, TAB Arbeitsbericht 25, Bonn.

Ratz, Erhard (ed.) (1995): *Zwischen Neutralität und Wertung: Zur Theorie und Praxis von Beratung in der Humangenetik*, Munich.

Rehmann-Sutter, Christoph and Müller, Hansjakob (eds) (1995): *Ethik und Gentherapie: Zum praktischen Diskurs um die molekulare Medizin*, Tübingen.

Rothstein, Mark A. (ed.) (1991): *Legal and Ethical Issues Raised by the Human Genome Project*, Houston, Texas.

Sass, Hans-Martin (ed.) (1991): *Genomanalyse und Gentherapie*, Berlin, Heidelberg and New York.

Sawicki, Jana (1991): *Disciplining Foucault. Feminism, Power, and the Body*, New York and London.

Schöne-Seifert, Bettina and Kruger, Lorenz (ed.) (1991): *Humangenetik – Ethische*

Probleme der Beratung, Diagnostik und Forschung, Stuttgart, Jena and New York.

Schulz, Ulrike (1991): *Gene mene mun, raus musst du. Von der Rassehygiene zu den Gen- und Reproduktionstechnologien*, Munich.

Shiva, Vandana and Moser, Inguun (eds) (1995): *Biopolitics*, London and New Jersey.

Ulanowsky, Carole (ed.) (1995): *The Family in the Age of Biotechnology*, Aldershot.

De Wachter (1993): *Experimental (Somatic) Gene Therapy*, Instituut voor Gezond-heidsethiek, Maastricht.

Waldschmidt, Anne (1996): *Das Subjekt in der Humangenetik*, Münster.

Walters, LeRoy and Palmer, Julie Gage (1997): *The Ethics of Human Gene Therapy*, New York and Oxford.

Weir, Robert F., Lawrence, Susan C. and Fales, Evan (ed.) (1994): *Genes and Human Self-Knowledge. Historical and Philosophical Reflections on Modern Genetics*, Iowa City.

Wess, Ludger (ed.) (1995): *Schöpfung nach Mass: perfekt oder pervers?*, Publik-Forum Spezial, Oberursel.

Wichterich, Christa (ed.) (1994): *Menschen nach Mass*, Göttingen.

Contributors

LISA SOWLE CAHILL is Associate Professor of Christian Ethics at Boston College. She received her doctorate in theology from the University of Chicago Divinity School in 1976, after completing a dissertation entitled *Euthanasia: A Protestant and a Catholic Perspective*. Recent research interests include method in theological ethics, the use of scripture in ethics, medical ethics, and sexual ethics. Articles on these subjects have appeared in American journals such as *Theological Studies, Journal of Religious Ethics, Journal of Medicine and Philosophy, Chicago Studies, Religious Studies Review, Interpretation, Horizons*, and *The Linacre Quarterly*. She has also written *Between the Sexes: Toward a Christian Ethics of Sexuality*. She also serves as an Associate Editor of *Journal of Religious Ethics, Religious Studies Review*, and *Horizons*.

Address: Boston College, Dept. of Theology, Chestnut Hill, Mass. 02167–3806, USA.

JULIE CLAGUE (born 1964) was brought up in Blackburn, England. After completing a chemistry degree she studied theology at Heythrop College, London. She is currently working towards her doctorate on the moral and political philosophy of Jacques Maritain at Cambridge, England. She teaches moral theology and applied ethics at St Mary's University College, Strawberry Hill. She has published a number of articles and reviews, including studies of *Evangelium Vitae; Veritatis Splendor*; the ARCIC Statement on Morals; and foetal tissue research.

Address: St Mary's University College, Waldegrave Road, Twickenham, TW1 4SX, England; e-mail: jpc28@cam.ac.uk.

SANDRO SPINSANTI studied psychology at the University of Rome La Sapienza and theology at the Pontifical Lateran University, specializing in moral theology. He has taught medical ethics in the medical faculty in the Catholic University of Rome and bioethics in the University of Florence, and has been director of the International Centre of Family Studies in Milan and of the Department of Human Sciences in the Fatebenefratelli Hospital in Rome. He is now Director of the Giano Institute for Medical Humanities and Health Management. He founded the medical humanities journal *L'Arco di Giano*, of which he is director, and is a member of the national commission for the fight against AIDS. His most recent publications include: *La bioetica. Biografie per una disciplina*, Milan 1995; *La bioetica nella professione infermieristica*, Naples 1995; *Il medico e il paziente, una relazione complessa*, Milan 1995; and *Management per la nuova sanità*, Naples 1997.

Address: Dir. Instituto Giano, Via Giusti 3, 00185 Rome, Italy.

STELLA REITER-THEIL studied philosophy and psychology at the University of Tübingen; from 1986 she taught ethics in medicine and psychology in German and Austrian universities; between 1990 and 1995, as General Secretary she was involved in setting up the Academy for Ethics in Medicine in the University of Göttingen and in numerous related projects; since 1995 she has been research referee at the newly-founded Centre for Ethics and Law in Medicine at the clinic of the University of Freiburg and has been responsible for national and European projects. Her works include *Ethik in der Medizin* (ed. with W. Kahlke), Stuttgart 1995; *Informed Consent in Psychiatry* (ed. with H. G. Koch and H. Helmchen), Baden-Baden 1996.

Address: Zentrum Ethik und Recht in der Medizin im Klinikum der Albert-Ludwigs-Universität, Elsässer Strasse 2m.Haus 1a, D 79110 Freiburg, Germany.

LIZ HEPBURN, a Loreto sister, is the Director of the Queensland Bioethics Centre which was established in 1981 by the Catholic bishops of Queensland. She has a background in science with a PhD in pharmacology from Monash University and qualifications in psychology, theology and education. She also has an MA in philosophy from Georgetown University and has been a visiting scholar at both Georgetown University and MacGill University. She is the author of *Of Life and Death*, published in 1996, and lectures and writes extensively in the field of bioethics.

Address: Queensland Bioethics Centre, 18 Clarence Street, PO Box 3343, South Brisbane, Queensland 4101, Australia.

MAUREEN JUNKER-KENNY, head of the School of Hebrew, Biblical and Theological Studies in Trinity College, Dublin, teaches Practical Theology and Christian Ethics. Her research areas include F. Schleiermacher and foundations of theology in Modernity, the communicative ethics of J. Habermas, and biomedical ethics.

Address; University of Dublin, School of Hebrew, Biblical & Theological Studies, Trinity College, Dublin 2, Ireland.

M. CATHLEEN KAVENY is Associate Professor of Law at the University of Notre Dame. She earned a PhD and a JD from Yale University. Before beginning her teaching career, she served as a law clerk for the Hon. John T. Noonan, Jr of the United States Court of Appeals for the Ninth Circuit, and practiced health care law with the law firm of Ropes & Gray in Boston. Her area of specialization is the intersection of law and morality. Her recent articles have dealt with such topics as affirmative action, health care reform, and physician-assisted suicide. She is currently preparing a book on post- liberal philosophy, American Constitutional law, and minority religious communities.

Address: University of Notre Dame Law School, Notre Dame IN, 46556–0780, USA.

MÁRCIO FABRI DOS ANJOS is a Redemptorist priest. He holds a doctorate of theology from the Gregorian in Rome and is President of the Brazilian Society of Theology and Sciences of Religion. Up to 1997 he was a member of the Brazilian National Commission for Ethics in Research. He lectures in moral theology in São Paulo and is a member of the Ethics Research Committee of the Santa Casa there. His books, as author or editor, are: *Teologia: Profissão* (1996); *Teologia e Novos Paradigmas* (1996); *Etica e Direito: um diálogo* (1996); also numerous articles, including 'Etica e Clongem na Questão dos Paradigmas' in *REB* 55, 1995, 217, 105–17.

Address: R. Oliveira Alves, 164, 04210-060 São Paulo, SP Brazil.

EBERHARD SCHOCKENHOFF was born in 1953. He is Professor of Moral Theology in the universities of Regensburg and Freiburg. His most important publications are: *Das umstrittene Gewissen*, Mainz 1990; *Sterbehilfe und Menschenwürde*, Regensburg 1991;*Ethik des Lebens*, Mainz 1993; *Naturrecht und Menschenwürde*, Mainz 1996.

Address: Institut für Systematische Theologie, Arbeitsbereich Moraltheologie. Albert-Ludwigs-Universität, 79085 Freiburg, Germany.

MAURA A. RYAN is Assistant Professor of Christian Ethics at the University of Notre Dame. Her research and teaching interests include Christian bioethics, Roman Catholic social thought and feminist ethics. She has published on ethical issues in assisted reproduction, population, assisted suicide and genetics.

Address: University of Notre Dame, Department of Theology, Notre Dame, IN 46556, USA.

MARCIANO VIDAL was born in S. Pedro de Trones, in the León region of Spain. He is a priest of the Redemptorist Congregation and a doctor of theology specializing in moral theology. He lectures at the Pontifical University of Comillas in Madrid and is director of and lecturer at the Redemptorists' Higher Institute of Moral Sciences there. His major publication is the four-volume manual of theological ethics, *Moral de Actitudes*, now in its eighth edition (1995). His most recent publications are a study of the family in the life and thought of St Alphonsus de Liguori (1995); an essay on conscientious objection (1995); an examination of the virtue and ethical principle of solidarity (1996); *La estimativa moral. Propuesto para la educación moral* (1997); and *Moral y espiritualidad* (1997). He is a director-counsellor member of the Board of Directors of *Concilium*.

Address: Manuel Silvela 14, 28010 Madrid, Spain.

SIGRID GRAUMANN was born in 1962 and studied biology in Tübingen, specializing in human genetics and philosophy. From 1994 to 1997 she was a member of the post-graduate group on 'Ethics in the Sciences' at the University of Tübingen's Centre for Ethics in the Sciences. She is working on a dissertation on scientific and ethical questions in gene therapy. Since 1997 she has been an academic assistant in the European Network of Biomedical Ethics.

CHRISTOF MANDRY was born in 1968 and studied Catholic theology and philosophy at the University of Tübingen and the Centre Sèvres in Paris. Since 1996 he has been an academic assistant in the European Network of Biomedical Ethics; he is also working on a dissertation on the relationship between theology and philosophy with reference to ethics.

Address: Zentrum für Ethik in den Wissenschaften, Keplerstrasse 17, D 72074 Tübingen, Germany.

The editors wish to thank the great number of colleagues who contributed in a most helpful way to the final project.

R. Crusz	Kelaniya	Sri Lanka
K. Demmer	Rome	Italy
V. Elizondo	San Antonio	USA
R. Gibellini	Brescia	Italy
H. Häring	Nijmegen	Netherlands
B. Kern	Mainz	Germany
N. Mette	Münster	Germany
G. Mora	Catalunya	Spain
J. Porter	Nashville	USA
D. N. Power	Washington	USA
C. Theobald	Paris	France
M. Vidal	Madrid	Spain
J. O. Beozzo	São Paulo	Brazil